MYTHS AND ENCHANTMENT TALES

Myths and Enchantment Tales

adapted from the
original text by

MARGARET EVANS PRICE

illustrated by EVELYN URBANOWICH

RAND McNALLY & COMPANY

New York   •   Chicago   •   San Francisco

TABLE OF CONTENTS

TABLE OF CONTENTS

LIST OF FULL-PAGE
ILLUSTRATIONS

LIST OF FULL-PAGE ILLUSTRATIONS

THE INTRODUCTION

THIS is a group of stories out of the great picture book of Nature. Some of them are myths—made-up stories, as fairy tales are made-up stories. Some of them are enchantment tales, or legends, which are not entirely imaginary, but have some real history in them. The one who sings us these fair marvels is Greece. She is a wonderful singer, with skillful hands that shape the figures of her myths out of clay. Have you ever seen her Apollo or her Diana? It was Apollo, driving his golden chariot across the violet meadows of the sky, with whom Clytie fell in love, sitting on the ground and gazing up at him until she turned into the yellow sunflower that we plant in our gardens. Another lover whom we know as a flower, Narcissus, was so foolish as to lose his heart to his own face when, leaning over the bank of a river, he saw it reflected in the water. Do you know the Greek statue of Niobe, the queenly mother, trying, all in vain, to shield her last little daughter of seven from the silver arrow of the angry Moon Goddess, Diana, whose brother, Apollo, had already slain with his bright shafts the poor mother's seven sons?

Greece has not only those deft hands that fashion images

9

of immortal beauty, but she has also deep, dark, dreaming eyes and a voice whose music has been heard around the world. If her dream is of that far-away time when gloomy vapors brooded over vast swamps and forests, she will sing of Prometheus, who brought the glorious gift of fire. If her dream is of the ocean, she may chant the peril of the princess chained to a rock overhanging the surf, an offering to the terrible sea-dragon already swimming along the coast to devour her.

And what happened then? That tuneful voice will tell you in the story of Perseus and Andromeda. Greece has many tales of ships and sailors and adventures on wild shores, for she sits where three seas, on her right hand and on her left and at her feet, whisper to her day and night of the wonders they have known. Sometimes her song will be of that enchanted island where Circe kept her court, changing men into beasts by the touch of her shimmering wand, until the wise Ulysses came with a magic mightier than hers; or, again, she will tell how this ever-wandering Ulysses, shipwrecked and forlorn, had courteous welcome and gracious aid from the young princess Nausicaa.

But this sea-loving singer takes pleasure, too, in her groves and gardens, her gray-leaved olives and tall rows of cypresses. She will tell you how Dryope lived in a lotus tree, and how the rough and wayward Erysichthon, hewing down an oak, killed with his reckless axe the lovely nymph who lived there. She will tell you, too, how the apple-cheeked Pomona, lady of orchards, was wooed and won, and of another lover, Pygmalion, who carved his bride out of ivory. Let us hope she made him less trouble than the bride Pandora made for her husband and for all the world.

And she has wonderful tales to tell of the sky above and of the world beneath the earth. When the weather went suddenly hot and the trees and crops were parched, it was because the boy Phaeton, rashly trying to drive his father's chariot, but unable to control the flaming steeds, had come too near the earth.

As often as the spring blossoms up from the ground, so often the stolen Proserpina returns from darkness to the light. When the orchard is carpeted with the "drifted snow of apple blossoms" and, later, when the hard green balls are mellowing into rosy fruit, Vertumnus, you may be sure, has been wooing Pomona.

The voice of Greece, which has been chanting on all day, becomes even sweeter with the sunset. As those amber glows spread through the western sky, she tells of King Midas, so poor in a world of gold, and of Jason, sailing away to snatch from the black dragon, Night, that very Golden Fleece before our eyes. As the moon rises, she throws her a kiss, singing of pale Diana in her car of pearl and of the shepherd Endymion, forever dreaming of her beauty as, forever young, he sleeps upon the mountain of their joy. Even after dusk has fallen and silenced the busy noises of the day, that tranquil voice intones the legend of Orpheus, the lute-player, who followed his Eurydice into the deepest of all shadows and proved to Death the enduring power of Love.

—Adapted from original introduction by
Katharine Lee Bates

DAEDALUS AND ICARUS

ONCE there was a famous architect and sculptor who lived in Athens. His name was Daedalus. He had as a pupil his nephew Talus, who was also very skillful. Daedalus soon began to fear his nephew's cleverness, because he didn't want anyone to be better than himself.

One day, Daedalus pushed Talus off a mountain top to his death. He had not, of course, planned to kill his nephew, but had done so in a jealous rage. Now there was nothing for him to do but flee, in order to save his own life. Taking his son, Icarus, he wandered from place to place, until he came to Crete.

King Minos of Crete was happy to see Daedalus, because the king wanted a special building designed and there was no one who could do it better than Daedalus. When the Labyrinth—for that is what the building was called—was finished, the king was delighted. But the king was so afraid someone in some other land might hear about this unusual building full of crisscrossing passages, that he kept Daedalus and Icarus prisoners in its tower.

From the little window of this lonely tower they could

see the blue ocean and watch the gulls and eagles sweep back and forth over the island.

Sometimes a ship sailed out toward other lands, and then Daedalus and Icarus would long for freedom, and wish that they might sail away and never again see the island of Crete.

Daedalus at last found a way for them to escape from the tower. But they had to hide themselves in the loneliest part of the island, because King Minos watched the coming and going of all ships, and so Daedalus and Icarus never found courage to go near the **harbor** where the **outgoing galleys** lay **anchored.**

Sometimes a ship sailed out toward other lands from

In spite of this, Icarus was almost happy. Besides the blue
sea, the ships, and the birds, which he loved to watch, he found
shellfish along the shore, crabs among the rocks, and many
other curious things.

But Daedalus grew more lonely and miserable and spent
all his time watching the gulls as they flew in the air, and
planning how he and Icarus might escape from the island.

One day Icarus was throwing stones at the gulls. He killed
one of the birds and brought it to his father.

"See how the feathers shine, and how long the wings are!"
said the boy.

the harbor where the outgoing galleys lay anchored

Daedalus took the bird in his hands and turned it over slowly, examining the wings.

"Now if we had wings," said Icarus, laughing, "we could fly away and be free."

For a long time his father sat silent, holding the dead bird. Now and then he looked up and watched other birds as they wheeled in the air over the sea and the island.

At last he thought of a plan and said softly to himself, "We shall have wings, too."

After that, Daedalus was idle no more. He plucked feathers from all the birds that Icarus could kill, and began to make two great wings. He fastened the feathers to a framework with melted wax and threads pulled from his linen mantle.

When these two wings were finished, Daedalus bound them on himself. He rose into the air, waving his arms, now up, now down, and went soaring far out over the water.

Icarus jumped about in delight, and shouted to his father to come back and make another pair of wings so that they might fly away and leave Crete forever.

When Daedalus had finished another pair of wings he bound the smaller pair on his son. Then he warned Icarus not to wander off alone in the air but to follow him closely.

"If you fly too low, the dampness of the sea will make your feathers heavy, and you will sink into the water," said Daedalus. "But if you fly too near the sun the heat will melt the wax and you will fall."

Icarus promised his father that he would fly neither too high nor too low. They took off from the highest cliff on the island and they flew away.

Icarus felt himself sinking, and fluttered his wings wildly

At first Icarus was obedient and followed close behind his father, but soon in the joy of flying he forgot all that his father had told him, and stretching his arms upward he went higher and higher into the heavens.

Daedalus called to him to return, but the wind passed so swiftly that it carried all sound away, and Icarus could not hear. His wings bore him higher and still higher into the region of the clouds. As he went up and up the air grew warmer and warmer, but still he forgot his father's warning and flew on.

Soon he saw feathers floating in the air around him and suddenly he remembered what his father had told him. He knew that the heat of the sun had melted the wax that held the feathers to the framework.

Finally Icarus felt himself sinking, and fluttered his wings wildly in an effort to fly, but such a storm of feathers swept around him that he could not see.

With a wild cry, turning and whirling through the sky, poor Icarus fell down into the blue waters of the sea—known ever since as the Icarian.

Daedalus heard his cry and flew to the spot, but nothing could be seen of Icarus or his wings except a handful of white feathers that floated on the water.

Sadly the father went on with his journey, and finally reached the shore of a friendly island. There he built a temple to Apollo and hung up his wings as an offering to the god. But ever after he mourned his son, and never again did he try to fly.

APOLLO AND DIANA

ONE day, on an island in the Sea of the Dawn, twins—a boy and a girl—were born. Their mother Latona named them Apollo and Diana.

Jupiter, the ruler of the gods, was fond of beautiful children, but Juno, his wife, was hard-hearted and liked much better to pet her peacock than to fondle the dearest baby that ever lived.

Jupiter sent many blessings and gifts to Apollo and Diana and often went down to earth to visit them. This made Juno very angry, because she did not like Jupiter to show kindness to anyone but herself.

The island on which Apollo and Diana were born was small and rocky, so aided by Jupiter, their mother crossed the Sea of the Dawn to another country where there was a fair garden with fruit and wild honey and many other pleasant things for Latona and her children.

Juno, looking down from Olympus, was angry and said, "Jupiter is visiting Apollo and Diana again."

She waited until Jupiter had returned to Mount Olympus, and then hurried down to earth. Changing herself into

19

fierce and dreadful forms, she frightened Latona so that she ran from the beautiful garden which Jupiter had found for her. Carrying the twins in her arms, she wandered far away through cold and desolate lands.

Juno followed and tormented Latona in many ways. Apollo and Diana were large and heavy to carry. But when Latona grew tired and tried to rest, Juno sent wild animals to howl horribly behind her and insects to sting her, so the poor mother, the twins pressed closely to her bosom, stumbled on, although she was ready to fall from weariness.

At last, footsore and thirsty, she came to a little pond of clear water and thought she might stop to rest and drink. On the shores of the pond a band of country people were cutting willows to make baskets. At once Juno filled their hearts with unkindness, and, throwing down their knives and willows, they shouted rudely at Latona and ordered her to leave.

"Go away from our lake," they said, and threatened to harm her if she did not go.

"But I am so thirsty," begged Latona.

"Ha, ha," cried the people, "then you may drink mud." And as they spoke they waded into the pond, stirring up the mud with sticks and with their feet until the cool waters of the little pond were no longer clear, but brown and dirty.

Latona stood up and, holding her head high in anger, said to them, "Since you like this lake so well you shall stay here forever."

As Latona spoke, the sky grew dark, the lightning flashed, and the thunder rumbled loudly overhead. The men and boys vanished, and their empty tunics floated on the muddy waters of the pond. Here and there above the water peeped the green head of a bullfrog. Latona in her anger had changed the country people into frogs.

When Jupiter learned that Latona, with Apollo and Diana, had been driven from the garden, he led them to a lovely mountain on the island of Delos, where Juno could not trouble them. There Latona dwelt happily in peace and quiet and cared for her children.

Before Apollo was ten years old he left his mother and his twin sister Diana and traveled to a fair and distant land, the home of the Hyperboreans, where spring lasted one half of the year and summer the other half.

When Apollo returned to Delos to see his mother and Diana he came riding over the water in a chariot drawn by white swans. Latona and Diana were glad to see him and were greatly interested in the chariot, which was wreathed with flowers. Apollo told them that Jupiter had given it to him so that he might return to visit them.

Jupiter saw Apollo as he unharnessed the swans from his chariot. His heart was filled with pride as he looked at the beautiful boy.

"The swan chariot will do for Apollo now," said the ruler of the gods, "but when he is grown, Helios shall rest, and Apollo shall drive the chariot of the sun.

"Instead of white swans I will give him swift horses. The flowers of the Hyperboreans may wreathe his chariot now, but I will give him a chariot wreathed in fire."

Long ago, Vulcan, the God of Fire, had made the chariot of the sun and bathed it in fire from his magic forge. Ever after the chariot flamed and glowed with a light that could not be put out. Hyperion was the first one to drive this wonderful chariot, and the next was Helios, his son. Helios had driven it for so many years that now he was weary and ready to rest.

When Apollo was grown, Jupiter sent for him and showed him the golden chariot.

"You shall harness your white swans no more!" said Jupiter. "Take the sun into your keeping, and drive the chariot of the sun and the four horses of the day!"

Apollo sprang into the chariot, amazed and delighted at its wonderful beauty. Helios showed him the way he must go, and watched the sun rise in the sky and journey toward the west, glad indeed that Apollo was old enough to drive, so that he might give up traveling and rest.

Apollo came riding over the water in a chariot drawn by swans

Diana drives her milk-white steeds across the broad heavens

That evening, when Apollo had returned his horses to their stables and had hidden his chariot behind banks of purple clouds, he hurried back to his mother and his sister Diana and told them of Jupiter's gift and of his journey across the heavens.

When Diana heard of the honor that had fallen to her brother, she was proud but also a little envious.

"You have journeyed to the land of the Hyperboreans and visited many other places that I have not seen," she said. "While I stayed with our mother and cheered her, you rode in your swan-drawn chariot wherever you wished, and now Jupiter gives you the chariot of the sun and four handsome horses to drive and gives nothing at all to me.

"Tomorrow before dawn, when you go to Mount Olympus, I am going with you. I shall remind Jupiter that I am your twin, and if you light the sky by day with the chariot

She lights the earth, sea, and heavens with soft, silvery light

of Helios, then I will ask him to let me light the heavens with silver fire while you rest."

In the morning Apollo rose early to present himself to Jupiter before starting out on his daily journey in the chariot. Diana rose also and went with him to Mount Olympus.

Jupiter was much surprised to see the fair twin sister of Apollo, for he had not thought of Diana for a long time. He remembered how lovely she had been when a child, and he saw that now she was even more beautiful.

When Jupiter heard that Diana wished to light the sky at night, he gave the silver orb of the moon into her keeping.

From that time on, every evening when Apollo has finished his travels and has hidden his lofty chariot behind the evening clouds, Diana drives her milk-white steeds across the broad pathway of heaven. Then, while her brother sleeps, she lights the earth and sea and heavens with her soft, silvery light.

CUPID AND APOLLO

C UPID was the baby son of Venus, the Goddess of Love and Beauty. Although his mother fed him daily with ambrosia and nectar, the food and drink of the gods, Cupid never seemed to grow. The years passed by, and still he remained a tiny, dimpled, laughing child, although he could fly and run wherever he wished and care for himself on earth as well as on Mount Olympus, the home of the Greek gods.

Apollo, God of Light, Healing, Music, and Poetry, also lived on Mount Olympus. He had great manly beauty, and was very fond of hunting with his bow and arrows.

Cupid loved to follow Apollo around, for he was fonder of him than of any of the other gods. He was much interested in Apollo's bow and arrows and longed to take them in his hand.

Once he saw Apollo take his strongest bow and his sharpest arrows and set out to kill a huge, dark monster called the Python.

The Python was a gloomy creature that breathed heavy smoke from his nostrils. This filled the air for miles around

26

with darkness, and the shadows were so heavy that no one standing in the valley could see the mountain tops.

As Apollo was the God of Light, he did not like the darkness, so he went straight into the shadowy valley, found the terrible Python, and killed him.

Cupid had followed him so quietly that Apollo did not know he was there until after the Python was killed, and the darkness had lifted from the valley. Then he saw the boy standing beside him.

"Oh, your arrows are wonderful!" cried Cupid. "Give me one! I'll do anything you say if you will only let me hold your bow."

But Apollo laughed, and taking Cupid's hand in his led him back to his mother.

Cupid was greatly disappointed and decided that if he could not have Apollo's bow and arrows he would get some for himself. He knew that almost anything he wished for, Vulcan could make at his anvil, for Vulcan was the God of Fire and of Metal-working. So one day Cupid asked Vulcan for a bow like Apollo's, and a quiver of golden arrows.

Vulcan fashioned a little bow, perfect and smooth and slender, and a quiver full of the sharpest, lightest arrows.

Venus, who was watching, gave to these darts a power no large arrows had ever possessed. When any one was touched ever so lightly by one of these golden arrows, he at once fell in love with the first person he saw.

Cupid was so delighted with his bow and arrows that he played with them from morning until night.

One day Apollo spent the day hunting through the forest.

In a little glade he came upon Cupid sitting on a mossy rock, playing with his bow and arrows. Apollo was much vexed to think that Cupid could handle so cleverly the same kind of weapons that he had used to kill the Python. He frowned, and spoke harshly to him.

"What have you to do with warlike weapons, saucy boy?" said Apollo. "Put them down and leave such things for grown people."

Cupid was hurt and angry. He had hoped Apollo would praise him for his skill, as Venus had done.

"Your arrows may have killed the Python," said Cupid, "but mine can wound you."

As he spoke he let fly an arrow, which struck Apollo so lightly it barely scratched him. Apollo laughed at him and walked on, not knowing what the wound really meant.

Soon he noticed a beautiful nymph gathering flowers in the forest. Her name was Daphne. Apollo had often seen her before, but she had never seemed so beautiful as now. He ran forward to speak to her. She saw him coming and was startled.

"Let me help you gather flowers," begged Apollo, but Daphne was so shy she ran away. Apollo wanted so much to be with her and talk to her that he ran after her.

Poor Daphne, terrified, ran faster and faster. When she was breathless and could run no more, she cried loudly to Peneus, the river god, for help.

Peneus was her father and, hearing his daughter's voice from far away, he thought she was in some terrible danger. Swiftly he sent his magic power over the forest, and to protect her changed her into a tree.

When Apollo reached out his hand to touch her, the fair maiden vanished.

Daphne's feet clung to the earth and took root. She felt the rough bark creeping over her shoulders and limbs. From her arms sprang branches, and her hands were filled with leaves. In her place stood a beautiful laurel tree.

"What have I done?" mourned Apollo.

He was so grieved and sad because he had brought this change on Daphne that he stayed by the tree all the afternoon, talking to it and begging Daphne to forgive him.

He asked for some of her laurel leaves that he might wear them on his head. Daphne shook her branches, and a little

The fair maiden vanished. In her place stood a beautiful tree

shower of leaves fell around Apollo. By this he knew that Daphne forgave him, and he gathered the leaves tenderly in his hands and wove them into a wreath.

Throwing aside a drooping wreath of flowers which he wore about his brow, Apollo placed the laurel on his head, where it remained forever fresh and green.

DIANA AND ACTAEON

In all the realm of King Cadmus of Thebes there was no hunter like young Prince Actaeon. The fiercest boars fell at the touch of his spear, so strong and sure was his thrust, and the dogs of his pack were not more swift in overtaking the deer than was Prince Actaeon himself.

Only one other excelled him in the hunt, but she was a goddess—Diana, Goddess of the Moon and of Hunting, twin sister of Apollo. Followed by her nymphs, the fair goddess loved to roam the woods and mountains by day, hunting until the noon sun was high overhead, and the heat became too great for comfort.

Then the nymphs laid aside their bows and arrows, their spears and their mantles, to rest in a glade deep in the forest. Diana had chosen this home for herself, and it was held sacred for her use.

No human being could go into the glade and remain alive. The very air of this charmed place was so clear and sweet, so cool and fragrant, that humans seemed to realize, as soon as they approached it, that here among the trees in this fair grove was the resting place of some deity. Therefore, they usually turned away from it reverently.

She seized one of the urns and dashed the water in Actaeon's face

But one day when the noon heat was great, Actaeon, tired of the hunt, left his comrades and, following a little brook, wandered away into the depths of the wood, seeking a cool and restful spot. He came at last to the edge of Diana's glade and heard the splashing of water and the merry voices of the nymphs at play.

Parting the branches of some laurel trees, he peeped through and saw a silvery fountain gushing from a rock, and a little pool of clear water where Diana and her nymphs were preparing to bathe. One nymph loosed the ribbon that bound Diana's hair, so that it fell in shining waves over her bare shoulders and floated around her like a golden cloud. Another nymph untied the thongs of Diana's sandals, while still another laid aside her mantle and held fresh linen for Diana to wear after her bath. Others busily drew water and filled great urns.

All these things Actaeon watched without thought of wrongdoing, until one of the nymphs happened to look toward the laurel trees and saw him peering out through the branches.

The nymph screamed, and ran to shield Diana from his curious gaze. The other maidens rushed also to screen the goddess, but it was too late!

A rosy color spread over Diana's cheeks and brow. Shame and anger were in her heart. She reached for her spear to kill Actaeon, but it lay far from her hand. Then she seized one of the urns and, raising it high above her head, dashed the water in Actaeon's face.

"Go, now," Diana cried, "and boast, if you can, of your boldness!"

Actaeon fell down on the bank of the little brook, and as he fell huge ears and branching antlers sprang from his head.

His arms became hairy, and hoofs took the place of his hands and feet. Gazing in the clear water of the little brook, he saw only a frightened stag that bounded away through the woods.

Back toward his comrades Actaeon ran, but at the sight of his dogs he felt a great fear and turned again into the forest. But the dogs had seen him and, leaping up at the sight of a deer, followed hard after poor Actaeon.

Never did he run so swiftly. Over rocks and hills and across streams he sped, with the fleetness of the wind, but still his dogs pursued him.

Now he thought sadly of how he himself had chased other deer, rejoicing to see them panting and weary. He remembered how often he had urged on his dogs and felt no pity.

As he ran Actaeon's heart beat wild and fast from fright and weariness, until at last, worn out, he fell to the earth, and the dogs overtook him.

His spirit passed from the body of the stag and slumbered ever after in the land of the shades.

Such was the harshness of the Goddess Diana to mortals who were over-bold.

PEGASUS AND BELLEROPHON

PEGASUS was a wonderful winged horse that belonged to Minerva, the gray-eyed goddess who watched over heroes and gave wisdom and skill to all those who truly wished it.

Now it happened that after Minerva had caught and tamed Pegasus, the winged horse, she did not care to ride him herself, but knew no human who deserved to own him. So Minerva gave Pegasus to the nymphs to care for until she could find a youth brave enough and wise enough to ride him.

The nymphs were happy caring for Pegasus. They brushed him, combed his mane, and fed him, but they knew that some day he would belong to a mortal master who would come and ride him away.

At last in Corinth there was born a little prince named Bellerophon. Glaucus, his father, had more skill in handling horses than any other man. As Bellerophon grew up, his father trained him and taught him all he knew, so that while Bellerophon was still very young he understood the ways of horses and learned to ride them.

All this time the winged horse was without a master.

When Bellerophon was sixteen he began to long for travel

and adventure in other lands, so he set out to visit a neighboring king.

Many friends came to bid the gallant young man goodby and wish him well, but there was one, named Proetus, who pretended to be Bellerophon's friend, but who really wished for him the worst that might happen. Proetus was jealous of Prince Bellerophon, and hoped that the young hero would not return from the journey.

It happened that Proetus was the son-in-law of Iobates, King of Lycia, and so, pretending friendship, Proetus gave Bellerophon a letter to carry to the king. Bellerophon, knowing

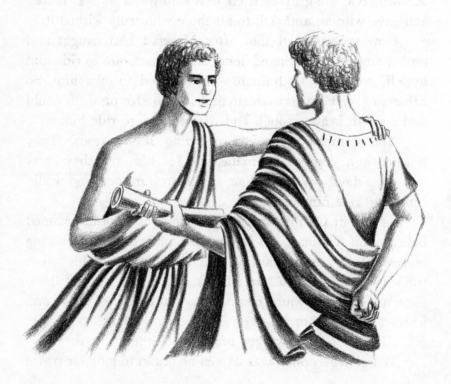

nothing of the wicked words that were in this letter, put it carefully in the pocket of his tunic and rode gayly away.

When he reached Lycia, the home of Iobates, he found great sorrow in the land and all the people mourning. Each night a monster called the Chimaera came down into the valley and carried off women and children, sheep and oxen. The mountain where he lived was white with the bones of his victims.

Bellerophon rode through the mourning city and came to the palace of the king. He presented himself to Iobates and gave him the letter.

As the king read, his face darkened and he seemed troubled, for the letter asked that Bellerophon should be put to death. The king did not like to heed the request in this strange letter, yet he wished to please his son-in-law. He knew that to kill a guest would be a wicked deed and against the laws of kindness to a visitor, and might also bring war on him from the land where the young prince lived. So he decided to send Bellerophon to slay the Chimaera, thinking he never could come back alive.

Bellerophon was not the least bit afraid, because he longed for adventure, and his heart was filled with a great desire to overcome this dark and evil monster, free the kingdom from fear, and make the mourning people happy.

But before starting out he found the oldest and wisest man in the whole kingdom and asked his advice. This aged man was named Polyidus. When he saw that Bellerophon was young and full of courage, yet humble enough to ask help from some one older, Polyidus told him a secret that no one else in the kingdom knew.

He told him of Minerva's winged horse, which he had
once seen drinking at a spring deep in the forest.

"If you sleep all night in Minerva's temple," said the old
man, "and offer gifts at her altar, she may help you to find
the horse."

Bellerophon went to the temple, and as he slept he
dreamed that he saw Minerva, clad in silver armor, her gray
eyes shining as if they held sparks of fire. Plumes of blue and

rose and violet floated from her helmet. She carried a golden bridle in her hand and told Bellerophon how he might reach the well where Pegasus came to drink.

When Bellerophon awakened, he saw the golden bridle on the temple floor beside him, and knew Minerva really had visited him. Then with the bridle over his arm he set out on his journey through the forest. When he found the well, he hid himself among the bushes near by to watch for the coming of the winged horse. Soon Bellerophon saw the winged horse flying far up in the sky. Nearer and nearer he wheeled until his silver feet touched the green grass beside the spring.

As Pegasus bent his head to drink, Bellerophon sprang from his hiding place and caught him by the mane. Before Pegasus knew what had happened, the golden bridle was slipped over his head, and Bellerophon had leaped to his back and was sitting between his outspread wings.

Pegasus rose into the air and darted wildly through the sky, now flying high among the clouds, now diving swiftly toward the earth. He reared and plunged, trying to shake Bellerophon from his back. He flew wildly over the sea and the mountains all the way to Africa and back. He flew over Thebes and over Corinth, and people looking up into the sky thought they saw some strange bird passing overhead.

But Bellerophon understood how to handle fierce horses, for he remembered the things his father had taught him. At last Pegasus knew he had found his master and, tired and panting, sank down to the grass beside the well.

After Pegasus had rested, Bellerophon armed himself with a long spear and rode toward the mountain where the Chimaera lived.

Bellerophon rode Pegasus as near as he dared and raised his spear

There on a ledge of rock outside his cave the monster lay basking in the sunlight. He was partly like a lion and partly like a dragon. He lay with his lion's head resting between his paws and his long green tail, like that of a lizard, curled around him.

Bellerophon rode his horse as near as he dared to the ledge on which the dragon lay, then raised his spear to strike at the Chimaera, but the great beast blew out clouds of smoke and fire, and Pegasus drew back in terror.

As the monster drew in his breath for another puff, Bellerophon rode close to the ledge and with one strong thrust sent his spear through the heart of the Chimaera.

When the young prince came back to the palace, riding the winged horse and carrying the head of the dreadful Chimaera, there was wild rejoicing in Lycia. Everyone admired and praised Bellerophon, and crowded around the wonderful horse, amazed at his wings and his silver feet.

The young daughter of King Iobates, who came out on the portico of the palace to see the hero and his horse, fell in love with Bellerophon the moment she saw the young warrior sitting so proudly between the white wings of Pegasus. King Iobates led her to Bellerophon and gave her to him for his bride.

For a long time they were happy together. Bellerophon and Pegasus went on many adventures, and when Iobates died Bellerophon became king.

At last one day Bellerophon thought of a most daring adventure. He decided he would try to ride Pegasus to Mount Olympus and visit the gods.

Minerva appeared and warned him that the gods would

be angry, but he mounted his horse and rose high into the clouds, urging Pegasus up toward the summit of Mount Olympus.

Jupiter, chief of the gods, looked down and, seeing the horse approaching, was angry to think that any mortal should dare approach the home of the gods. He caused a gadfly to light on Pegasus and sting his neck, his shoulders, and his nose.

Pegasus was so startled by this that at once he reared and wheeled among the clouds, leaping wildly in the air, and Bellerophon was thrown from his back and dropped down to earth.

Minerva, causing him to land where the ground was soft, spared his life, but as long as he lived Bellerophon wandered, crippled and lonely, seeking all over the earth for his wonderful winged horse.

But Pegasus never again returned to him.

PROMETHEUS

BEFORE Jupiter became chief of all the gods on Mount Olympus, there were other gods—children of the Sky and of the Earth. Some of them were called Titans and they were savage and cruel.

For ten years, Jupiter, with his brothers and sisters, fought against the Titans. Finally, with the help of one-eyed giants called Cyclops, the Titans were defeated. Then Jupiter sent the Titans to a fiery prison in the underworld.

One of these Titans was Iapetus. He had three sons. One was Atlas who fought with his father against Jupiter, and he was punished by being forced to hold the sky on his shoulders. The other two sons were Prometheus and Epimetheus. Prometheus was very wise. He guessed that Jupiter would win the war and so decided to fight on his side, and he got his brother Epimetheus to do the same.

When there was peace again, and Jupiter sat on his throne on Mount Olympus, he sent for Prometheus. In gratitude for his help, Jupiter gave Prometheus great power. He sent him to Earth and told him to make mortal man out of clay. Jupiter told Prometheus that when he had made his statues of men out of clay, he, Jupiter, would breathe life into them. There were to be only men—no women or children.

Then Jupiter told Prometheus that he could teach the mortals anything they needed to know in order to live, and he was also to teach them the arts so that they could build beautiful temples to honor the gods.

"You may give the mortals any gift except the gift of fire," said Jupiter. "Fire belongs to the gods only, and must be kept on Mount Olympus."

Prometheus was happy to be of benefit to man. He taught people how to make their own tools and how to build homes for themselves. He taught them how to plant and grow their own food, and he taught them how to use animals to make their work easier. He even taught them how to make music and how to paint.

But without fire, life on earth was very difficult. Food had to be eaten raw; houses could not be kept warm. Also tools had to be of stone because there was no fire for working metal.

Minerva, daughter of Jupiter, had been watching over Prometheus and had helped him in his work. Now, because Prometheus was kind, and wanted man to be comfortable on earth, he called upon Minerva to help him to get fire from Mount Olympus. She knew that Jupiter was away and promised to lead Prometheus to Mount Olympus by a secret path.

Before leaving, Prometheus called his brother Epimetheus to him, to tell him what he was going to do.

"My brother," said Prometheus, "I know that when I steal the fire from the heavens Jupiter will be very angry. He will, I am sure, punish me severely. I am willing to accept punishment if you will promise to take my place. I love the people

I have created out of clay and want to be sure that you will carry on my work."

Epimetheus gave his promise sadly. Then Prometheus added, "Be very careful when I am gone. Be sure, above all, that you do not accept any gift from Jupiter, because any gift from him will be evil. When he is angry, he is greatly to be feared."

Then Minerva led Prometheus to Mount Olympus. Just as he arrived, Apollo came back from his day's journey in his chariot of the sun. Prometheus lit a torch from the chariot, and

Prometheus stayed chained to the rock for many years

hid the fire in a hollow stalk that he concealed under his cloak. Then Prometheus stole away without being seen by any of the gods, and brought his fire to earth.

Prometheus lit the first campfire on earth. At first the people were afraid of it, but they trusted Prometheus, so they came closer and closer and enjoyed its pleasant warmth and its beautiful glow.

Quickly, because he knew that he would not have much time before Jupiter discovered that he had been disobeyed, Prometheus taught the mortals how to use this gift of fire. He knew that powerful as Jupiter was, once a gift had been given, he could not take it away.

Soon Jupiter returned to Mount Olympus. Looking down to earth at night, he saw sparks of light from the campfires and knew that Prometheus had stolen the fire.

He was angrier than he had ever been before, and called his son Vulcan, God of Metal-working. When Vulcan was before him, Jupiter commanded:

"Go down to earth and capture Prometheus. Carry him to the great mountain at the edge of the world and forge a metal chain that cannot be broken. Bind Prometheus to a rock with this chain, and leave him there. He shall stay there forever, for he is an Immortal, and cannot die. He will freeze in winter and be scorched by the sun in summer. He will be an example to any who dare to disobey the God of the Heavens."

Vulcan sorrowfully carried out his father's wishes, and Prometheus did stay chained to the rock for many years. But he was, at last, freed by Hercules.

PANDORA AND THE GOLDEN BOX

Not satisfied with inflicting terrible punishment on Prometheus for stealing fire from heaven, Jupiter thought about ways to upset the work Prometheus had done among men. At last he thought of a scheme.

Jupiter decided that he would create a woman and send her to earth. So he ordered his son Vulcan, who was especially clever with his hands, to fashion a woman out of clay.

When the clay statue was ready, Jupiter called upon the four winds to blow life into it, and he named the woman Pandora, which means "all-gifted," for Jupiter intended that each of the gods was to bestow on her a special gift.

Venus gave Pandora unusual beauty, Minerva dressed her in fine clothes, and then Jupiter and the other gods made her silly and unwise, curious, lazy, and troublesome. So Pandora was lovely to look at, but not at all likable.

Then Jupiter had Mercury take Pandora to earth and present her to Epimetheus, Prometheus's brother, as his bride. Jupiter intended that Pandora should cause much trouble among mankind, because this was his way of taking revenge against Prometheus who was much loved by the mortals he had created at Jupiter's command.

Hope was the last to come out, so the mortals didn't suffer so much

Epimetheus did not, of course, know what Jupiter had in mind and Pandora was so beautiful that he immediately fell in love with her. Epimetheus remembered that Prometheus had warned him to accept no gift from Jupiter. But he hoped that by doing as Jupiter wished he might make the chief of the gods sorry for what he had done to Prometheus. And besides, Pandora was so fair to look upon that Epimetheus could not resist her.

Now it happened that when Prometheus went to Mount Olympus he had left with Epimetheus a box made of gold. Prometheus had said that the box must never be opened by anyone, and not even Epimetheus knew what the box contained.

Pandora saw the box and, since she had been given a strong sense of curiosity, was most unhappy when her husband told her that she could not open it. She could hardly keep her hands off it, and one day when her husband was away she decided that she would lift the lid just a little and peek inside.

All at once, out of the box came, with a rush, all the unpleasant things that Prometheus had carefully put away so that mortals would not be troubled with them—sickness and sadness, jealousy and hate, lies and cheating, and all the other evils you can name. All of these ills infected mankind, and Jupiter, looking down, was pleased that Pandora had accomplished the purpose for which he had sent her to earth.

But Prometheus was very wise. He knew that Jupiter would find some way to undo the good work he had done. And so, with all the evil things, he had imprisoned Hope in the box as well. Hope was the last to come out, so the mortals did not suffer quite as much as they would have without it.

HERCULES

WHEN Hercules was a baby he lived in the palace of Amphitryon, King of Thebes. Although Amphitryon loved the baby dearly and provided many women to wait on him and care for him, Hercules was not his own child. He was the son of the great god Jupiter, king of the heavens, and of Alcmene, granddaughter of Perseus.

King Amphitryon was proud of him because he was much larger and stronger than other babies, but Juno, who was the queen of all the goddesses, hated this little son of Jupiter.

One day the goddess sent two great serpents to destroy Hercules as he lay in his cradle, but Hercules wakened as the serpents rustled over his linen coverlet, and, reaching out his strong little hands, he grasped them around the neck and held them tight until they were strangled. His nurses, hearing him chuckle, knew his nap was over, so they came in to take him up. There lay the two serpents dead in his cradle!

This was such a wonderful thing for a baby to do, that King Amphitryon boasted of it all over his kingdom. As Hercules grew older, the king found the wisest teachers to train him in all the ways in which a prince should be trained. He learned quickly, and soon his skill was talked of up and down the land.

Before Hercules's birth, Juno had made Jupiter promise that the first male descendant of Perseus should be High King, and any other descendants of Perseus would be his subjects. It so happened that Eurystheus was born just an hour before Hercules. So Eurystheus was made King of Mycenae, and Hercules was one of his subjects.

Eurystheus was jealous of Hercules because Hercules was much stronger and much more famous than the king. So the king decided that he would force some strenuous tasks on Hercules, feeling sure that one of them, at least, would prove so dangerous that Hercules would lose his life.

These tasks came to be known as "the twelve labors of Hercules." Hercules had no choice, of course. He had to follow his king's orders.

The first of these adventures was a fight with a terrible lion that lived in the valley of Nemea. When he failed to kill it with his club, Hercules strangled it with his hands, and returned carrying the body of the great beast across his shoulders.

Next he killed a nine-headed water serpent called the Hydra, which lived in the country of Argos; and then he captured a boar that had long overrun the mountains of Arcadia, frightening and killing the people.

From one of his adventures he returned bringing a wonderful stag, with antlers of gold and feet of brass, which lived in the hills about Arcadia.

Then he was sent to clean the stables of King Augeas, who had a herd of three thousand oxen, whose stalls had not been cleaned in thirty years.

Hercules cleverly thought of a way to clean the filthy stables without even entering them. He dug a wide ditch from a river to the stables, and let the waters rush through the stalls into a ditch on the other side and down the hill into another river.

In a few hours the stables were clean. Then Hercules walled up the opening between the first river and the ditch so that no more water could flow through. When King Augeas came to look at his stables, much to his astonishment he found them clean and dry.

After Hercules had performed ten of these labors, Eurystheus began to lose hope. So he tried to think of something
more dangerous than all of the other adventures combined.

Hercules was sent to the western edge of the world, to the
Garden of the Hesperides, to find the golden apples that were
guarded by several nymphs and by a great, never-sleeping
dragon that coiled itself among the trees of the garden.

Hercules did not know where this sacred garden was. But he set out toward the west, and in his wanderings came to a mountain. On one of its highest peaks, Hercules saw Prometheus bound to a rock. Prometheus had stolen fire from Mount Olympus. This had made Jupiter angry, and he had ordered his punishment.

Hercules urged his father to give him permission to break the chains that held Prometheus, and set him free. Jupiter agreed, and Prometheus, after his long punishment, was unbound.

Out of gratitude, Prometheus told Hercules how to find the garden of the golden apples.

"You will find it," Prometheus said, "at the place where my brother Atlas stands, holding the weight of the heavens on his shoulders."

Hercules started out once more and, at last, he found Atlas.

Atlas was so eager to be released from the burden of the sky and the stars, that he promised to do anything Hercules wished if only he might once more be free.

So Hercules agreed to take the weight of the heavens on his own shoulders, if Atlas would get him some of the golden apples. This Atlas could do, because the nymphs who guarded the apples were his daughters, and with their help, Atlas could put the dragon to sleep.

Atlas stepped out, shaking his head wildly, shouting and leaping with gladness at being free once more. He went joyously across the land, splashing through cool streams and striding through the green grass.

Hercules held the heavens until Atlas finally returned

Hercules held the heavens until Atlas returned with the apples

with his big hands and deep pockets filled with golden apples. Atlas begged that he might carry them to Hercules's land and deliver them. But Hercules was afraid that if Atlas went he might never come back, so he asked Atlas to hold the earth until he rested his shoulders. He then set the sky again on the giant's shoulders and went back to Thebes with the golden apples.

When Hercules arrived with the apples, Eurystheus began to realize that there was nothing he could think of that would be too much for the hero. But he decided to try just once more.

This time the king sent him to the gates of Hell, to bring back Cerberus, the three-headed dog that guarded the gates. When Hercules was able to do even this, Eurystheus gave up.

At last, after many glorious labors, Hercules was carried to Mount Olympus in Jupiter's own chariot, and became one of the Immortals.

ADMETUS AND ALCESTIS

O NCE, on an April morning when the skies of Greece were
their bluest and the violets beside the River Amphrysus
only a shade duller than the sky, when the young white lambs
were wild with gayety and happiness, King Admetus rode
forth to see his flocks.

The king's herdsmen and shepherds bowed before him as
he rode through the green pastures and down the beautiful
valleys.

Most kingly he looked, with the glory of the spring sun
on his fair hair, and his many-hued mantle fluttering behind
like a banner in the wind.

Now and then he reined his great horse and spoke with
a shepherd or watched the lambs and ewes.

As he rode, he followed the river, and suddenly he saw a
strange shepherd sitting alone by the stream, playing on a lyre
and singing to himself. As he bent his golden head above his
lyre, the sheep that he should have been watching were straying to the farthest ends of the field.

He was so intent upon his song that he did not hear the
steps of the king's horse, thudding softly on the moist grass,

Suddenly King Admetus saw a strange shepherd playing his lyre

but continued to sing and touch the strings of his lyre, while King Admetus sat silent and listened.

The shepherd's music was so lovely that tears came to the king's eyes, and he felt as though his heart would break. The young king's thoughts turned to his beloved Alcestis, the daughter of King Pelias.

Admetus and Alcestis had loved each other since their first meeting. No other suitor seemed to Alcestis so noble or so kingly, and she would gladly have gone with him to his palace to be his bride and rule with him over Thessaly, but Pelias, her father, loved her so mightily and so selfishly that he could not bear to have her leave him even to marry the beloved of her heart.

King Pelias planned a way to keep all suitors from winning Alcestis. He promised her to the lover who would come to claim her riding in a chariot drawn by lions and boars.

No mortal suitor could tame or harness these fierce beasts, so Pelias thought that he was sure to keep his lovely daughter forever with him.

But even his cleverest plans could not lessen the love of Alcestis for Admetus, nor prevent her from thinking of him and longing for him.

As for King Admetus, every beautiful sight, every lovely sound recalled Alcestis to his mind, and never had he felt so close to her as when he heard the strange shepherd playing by the river. It was as if Alcestis rode at his side. He could see her glorious smile, warm as the spring sun, and her lovely eyes, blue as the violets around his horse's feet.

There was such magic in the shepherd's playing that, as Zephyr, the soft wind, passed through the trees with a gentle rustle, the waving and bending of the tall grass marking his pathway, Admetus could almost feel the silken touch of Alcestis's hair blown across his cheek.

"Arise, strange shepherd!" cried the king. "Who are you, and from what land have you come to tend my flocks?"

The shepherd looked up and, seeing the king, arose. He was taller than Admetus, broader of shoulder, and beautiful beyond the beauty of mortal shepherd.

"He is more like a prince than a herder of flocks," thought Admetus.

"Who are you?" he asked again.

The stranger bowed his head and answered humbly, "Your servant, King Admetus."

Now the king was wise and skilled in reading the hearts of men, and he guessed that this was no servant but perhaps some noble youth or even a god.

He bade the shepherd follow him, and set another, more lowly but more watchful, to herd the straying flocks.

He led the stranger to his palace and gave him a white linen robe, taking away his ragged tunic. His maidens set food before the shepherd, serving him with bread and honey and the juice of grapes.

When he had finished eating, Admetus bade him play again. Once more the youthful shepherd touched his lyre, and again the king felt the near presence of his beloved like a perfume beside him.

Day after day the shepherd dwelt with the king, singing or playing his lyre at his master's command. They walked together over the flower-strewn fields or rode beside the river, talking and singing and watching the lambs.

Admetus gave the stranger the stewardship over all the other shepherds and over all his flocks, and indeed, although at first he seemed careless, letting his sheep stray and wander where they chose, yet he had a strange power over all the flocks. An ailing ewe became well at the touch of his hands. The lambs in King Admetus's flocks grew as no other lambs ever before had grown. Their fleece was white and soft as creamy silk, and not one lamb perished or strayed beyond the safety of the valley.

The king grew exceedingly fond of the shepherd and, walking with him in the fields, told him his most beautiful thoughts. He spoke of his love for Alcestis and of the hopelessness of winning her.

"How can any mortal harness lions and boars, or train them to draw a chariot?" he asked.

The shepherd smiled, and agreed that it was not a task for mortals.

The next day the chief shepherd was missing. Admetus thought sadly that his last blessing, his greatest human comfort, had vanished from him. He thought the gracious singer had gone on to other realms. The king then gave himself up to sorrow, and walked no more among his flocks nor rode beside the River Amphrysus, where first he had found the noble shepherd.

Instead, he sat in his courtyard grieving now for both Alcestis and his friend. The roses in his garden flung their perfume toward him. The birds sang; the tall, dark cedars cast their lovely blue and purple shadows on the ivory pillars of his palace and gave back their images in the garden pool, but Admetus did not lift his head or cease grieving.

At last one day came a shouting and wild commotion. Servants burst through his high garden gates, screaming in terror.

"Lions are coming, and boars!" they cried. "Run! Run!"

They were so frightened that they did not look twice, or they would have seen the chariot, the harness, and the driver who held the reins of those strange beasts that came running toward the palace.

King Admetus rose and went to shut the gates of the garden. Looking down the broad white road, he saw the shepherd whom he loved, driving his chariot toward the palace. He saw the lions and boars harnessed together, and knew that now he might go to ask for Alcestis.

His heart leaped to meet the shepherd, and his feet carried him toward the chariot with the speed of the wind.

Forgetting that he was king, the other a servant, he embraced his beloved shepherd and thanked him, then leaped into the chariot and drove off in a cloud of white dust toward the kingdom of Pelias.

He made no stops on the long journey, though his throat was dry with the dust of the road, and the vineyards that he passed hung heavy with cooling grapes; though the wayside fountains splashed crystal and clear, and the shade of the tall trees invited him to refreshing rest.

Only when he neared the kingdom of Pelias did he pause. Then, still holding the reins of his strange steeds, he bent over a little stream and washed the dust from his brow, the stains from his hands, that Alcestis might see him, not as a dusty traveler, but as a king.

Now it happened that Alcestis on that day sat weaving in

The colored yarns fell from her lap in a bright heap on the floor

her tower with her maidens about her. She moved her shuttle back and forth, blending bright-hued threads into lovely patterns, thinking of her lover, and hoping, as maidens do, that her handiwork, the web in the loom, might find a place in his palace if ever the gods were kind and she went to be the bride of King Admetus. As she worked, a maiden idling near the window cried out and pointed down the road.

There, speeding toward the palace, Alcestis beheld Admetus in his chariot drawn by those fierce beasts which her father thought could never be driven together, now tamed and broken to harness and bringing her beloved swiftly nearer and nearer to her side.

She dropped her shuttle. The colored yarns fell from her lap in a bright heap to the floor. She called to her father, ran down from her tower, and out into the courtyard to meet Admetus.

Great was King Pelias's sorrow that Alcestis must leave him, but he kept his word, and that evening Admetus and Alcestis were wed.

In the morning Admetus led his bride to the strange chariot. He touched one of the great lions on the head, and the beast fawned and drooped his neck as a gentle horse might do. He spoke to the boars, and they rubbed their heads against him.

He lifted Alcestis into the chariot and drove away to his own kingdom, where the shepherd awaited them.

The palace was wreathed and garlanded with flowers. A banquet lay ready, and sweet music sounded through the hallways and chambers. The shepherd had prepared everything for the homecoming of Alcestis. Thereafter the king loved the shepherd more dearly than ever.

Peace and perfect happiness reigned in the palace of Admetus. It was as if the blessing of some god had fallen on King Admetus, so that everything he touched seemed to prosper. His flocks increased wonderfully. His harvests were rich beyond belief, and love and joy filled his heart.

But one day Admetus fell ill. Not one of the wise men in his kingdom could cure him or even say what his ailment was. The shepherd laid aside his lyre and stayed by the king's couch. He comforted Alcestis and helped her as she nursed Admetus.

But here that skill which had cured the sick ewes seemed powerless. The king grew worse, and sorrow fell upon the palace.

One evening the shepherd arose and went away, saying nothing of his purpose. Then, indeed, if any had watched him as he departed, they would have known that the strange shepherd was more than mortal.

Rising into the air, he disappeared in the low-hanging sunset clouds. He flew with great speed to the cavern of the Three Fates, Clotho, Lachesis, and Atropos.

It was Clotho who spun the bright threads of youth, Lachesis who wound them on her spindle, and Atropos, the eldest, who cut them with her slender shears.

As the shepherd entered their cave, the aged Atropos raised her head and blinked, as one who is blinded by the sunlight, but the younger Fates smiled and turned joyfully toward the visitor.

"Apollo, God of the Sun, why do you come to our cavern?" croaked Atropos.

"O Atropos," said Apollo, he who seemed but a shepherd

on earth, "O Atropos, you hold in your hands a life thread which you are about to cut. Stay your hand and return your thread to Lachesis, that King Admetus may live!"

Clotho and Lachesis, seeming to agree with their glorious visitor, held out their hands to stay their sister as she held her shears ready to close upon the slender life thread of King Admetus.

"I will spare him," croaked Atropos, "if some one else will die in his stead."

"There are many who would do that," answered Apollo.

"Find one before nightfall," warned Atropos as Apollo flew away.

He hurried to the palace and told the courtiers and servants that the king might live if one of them would die.

"Die for him yourself, young shepherd," said one. But Apollo, being an immortal, could not do this. He went all over the palace, except to the chamber where Admetus lay, looking for some one who loved Admetus enough to die for him. He sought in the farthest borders of the kingdom. Everyone was sorry to hear that the king was dying, but he found no one who was willing to give up his own life to save him.

The afternoon was almost gone, and Apollo, grieving and heartsick, went to the chamber of the king.

Alcestis sat beside him, tired and very white. Apollo told her what he had told everyone in the kingdom.

"Let me die for him!" said Alcestis. "Oh, I am so glad that he will live!"

Immediately, far away in their lonely home, the Three Fates heard. At the same moment Admetus opened his eyes and smiled at Alcestis.

A little glow of pink came into his cheeks, and strength returned to him, but every hour Alcestis grew whiter, until soon she lay on the couch from which Admetus had risen.

When the king heard that she had offered to die in his place, he wished that he might be ill again, and Alcestis well, but the promise had been given, and nothing could be done.

Now it happened just at this time that Hercules, the strongest of heroes, was passing through the country and stopped at the palace to rest. He heard the sounds of mourning, and was told that the lovely Queen Alcestis was dying. He asked the servants to show him her chamber, and with a grim look on his face, he sat down outside her door. For hours he sat there waiting. The people of the palace walked past him on tiptoe and wondered why he watched at the door.

No sound came from the room. Everything was quiet.

At last the sky grew dark, and Death, the messenger of Atropos, entered the palace to carry away the spirit of Alcestis. Through the wide gates he passed, invisible, and up the marble stairs. Like a rude winter wind he swept down the corridor to Alcestis's door.

Hercules felt him coming and arose to meet him. He stretched his arms across the door, and as Death tried to press past him, he caught him and wrestled with him.

At the touch of Hercules, Death became visible. His black garments whirled about them in great folds as they fought.

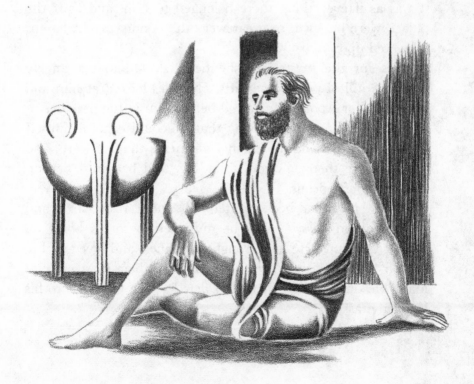

When a bit of cloth so much as touched Hercules, he felt as if an icy branch had struck him. When he seized Death by the throat, it was like grasping a huge icicle.

At last Hercules overcame Death and threw him rattling out of the palace, his black garments torn to shreds and half his bones broken.

He limped back to Atropos, and no amount of commanding or threatening would induce him to return.

The color came flooding back into the white cheeks of Alcestis. She sat up, and, feeling strength stealing back to her limbs, arose from her couch and smiled upon King Admetus. The king was wild with happiness. Again and again he poured out his thanks to Hercules and to his beloved shepherd.

Thereafter, when Hercules passed through the kingdom, it was as if everything there belonged to him, and as if the palace were his own, so great were the honors that Admetus showered upon him.

As for the mysterious shepherd, so tall and strangely noble, so full of power and gifts, Hercules looked at him and knew him for Apollo. He bowed before him in the presence of the king, and Apollo, knowing that he could conceal himself no longer, laid aside the earthly garments that he wore, and shone before them, glorious, blinding, and beautiful beyond the beauty of mortals.

But Apollo had been granted only one year on earth, and that year had passed. Now he must return to his home on Mount Olympus. He had brought happiness and love and life itself to Admetus and Alcestis, so, bidding them farewell with many blessings, he left them and flew back to Olympus to his heavenly tasks.

PROSERPINA AND PLUTO

PLUTO was God of Erebus, the world that lies beneath the ground. In his realm all was dark, misty, and gloomy. There was no sunshine there, nor any light except the glow of fires. Instead of blue sky overhead, he had only a roof of damp and dripping earth. There were no gay flowers in his kingdom, nor tall branching trees, nor green grass.

In some places the dripping water mingled with rust-colored lime from the earth, and hardened into all sorts of shapes. It made columns and arches and mounds, or hung like icicles in long, thin pendants from the roofs of Pluto's many caverns. There were black marble rocks in Erebus, and deep, dark lakes.

It would have been a dreary place for an earth child, but Pluto thought his kingdom the most beautiful in the world.

He thought his caves hung with lime crystals far lovelier than forests of birch trees. He liked the noiseless peace of the dim caverns. No songs of birds, no rustle of wind among the trees, disturbed their quiet. Only at times he heard far off the barking of Cerberus, the three-headed dog that guarded the entrance to his kingdom.

73

To drive away the dampness in the caves, Pluto lit many fires. Their flickering flames made the lime crystals sparkle and glimmer on the dark waters of the lakes. These fires were silent, too. They never made the cheerful, crackling noises that earth fires make.

The god of this strange, quiet land was content to stay in his own kingdom and seldom journeyed to the earth, which seemed a noisy place after the deep silence of Erebus.

But once Jupiter imprisoned four great giants in a cavern in Mount Aetna. In their anger the giants stamped their feet and shook the earth, raging back and forth and beating on the walls of their prison, or heaving their mighty shoulders against the sides of the cavern until the mountain trembled.

Far off in his kingdom under the ground Pluto heard these rumblings and feared that the surface of the earth might crack and the light of day break through into Erebus.

So, mounting his chariot drawn by four black horses, he journeyed swiftly up to earth and rode here and there to see how much damage had been done by the angry giants.

He found temples overturned, trees uprooted, and rocks thrown about as though some great earthquake had shaken the land, but no cracks deep enough to disturb the gloom of Erebus.

Pluto was preparing to return home, for the light of the sun was painful to his eyes, and he did not like the strange perfume of the earth flowers nor the sound of wind in the trees. But Cupid, that mischievous god of love, had other plans for Pluto.

He drew his bow, wounding the god of darkness with one of those arrows which cause the wounded one to love the first person he meets.

Pluto had just grasped the reins of his four black horses to turn them homeward, when he saw Proserpina, the daughter of Ceres, Goddess of the Harvest, with half a dozen nymphs dancing across the valley. Proserpina's hair floated behind her, bright as a flame of golden fire, and her eyes were as black as Pluto's lakes. She came nearer, gathering flowers and twining them into garlands.

The god of the dark kingdom stepped from his chariot and left it hidden among the trees. His cloak waved about him in many points and folds, thin and fluttering like a garment of smoke. Little tongues of fire rose from his crown and flickered above his forehead.

Proserpina and the nymphs saw him and drew back in alarm. Pluto strode toward them and seized Proserpina by the wrist. He did not woo her gently and kindly as lovers do. He said nothing at all, but lifted her in his arms and carried her off into the forest. He stepped into his chariot, seized the reins with one hand, and held Proserpina with the other. The four black horses sprang forward with a bound, galloping madly away toward the River Cyane.

Proserpina screamed for help. She cried to Ceres, her mother, but Pluto urged his horses on, and the chariot dashed away still faster.

When they reached the edge of the River Cyane, Pluto commanded the waters to open so that he might pass, but the river nymph saw that Proserpina was being carried away, and refused to help Pluto or make a pathway for him to cross.

Then in anger Pluto struck the ground with his mighty three-pronged spear, and the earth itself opened. The horses plunged downward, and with the chariot rattling from side to side, disappeared in the darkness.

Now, far off, Ceres had heard Proserpina's cry as Pluto carried her away. A sharp pain shot through the mother's heart, and like a bird she flew through forest and valley seeking Proserpina. She climbed mountains and crossed rivers, asking everyone she met for tidings of Proserpina, but neither man nor god would tell her where Pluto had carried her daughter, for everyone feared Pluto's anger.

A long, dark cloak hid Ceres's face and the brightness of her hair. No one who saw her then would have known that she

Pluto struck the ground, the earth opened, the horses plunged down

was the glowing Goddess of the Harvest. For many days she wandered over the earth, refusing in her sorrow to taste either ambrosia or nectar.

At last she came to the banks of the River Cyane, but the river nymph, also afraid of Pluto's wrath, dared not tell Ceres where the missing Proserpina was hidden. But it happened that as Pluto's horses had dashed down into the earth, Proserpina's girdle, loosened by her struggle to free herself, fell

from the chariot and lay on the river bank. The river nymph now took this girdle and floated it to where Ceres stood mourning at the water's edge.

Ceres saw it, and now her grief was more terrible than ever. She knew now that her daughter was gone, but still did not know that Pluto had taken her. In her sorrow, Ceres took away her blessing from the earth and cast an evil spell on the fruits and crops.

The leaves of the trees lost their green and began to fall in clouds of yellow. The blue sky grew angry and gray, and a cold wind swept over the earth. The nymphs shivered and wrapped their thin robes around them.

Everything became dry and withered, and famine and sickness and grief were over the whole earth.

Then the fountain, Arethusa, spoke to Ceres and told her where Proserpina was. "I come from far down in the earth," sang the fountain. "My waters have trickled through the realms of Pluto. I have seen your daughter. I have seen Proserpina, the beautiful, the bright, sitting on a black marble throne, queen of the spirits that wander silently between the crystal pillars and the flickering fires, and float over the lakes from which my waters rise."

When Ceres heard this, she raised her arms to Jupiter and begged him to return Proserpina to the earth.

"Never again," she cried, "will I make the corn grow or the ripening grain bend in golden waves. Unless my daughter is restored to me, never again will I watch over the harvest. The fruits of the earth shall remain withered, and man will die from hunger."

Jupiter knew that Ceres would do as she threatened, so he

sent Mercury, the speedy messenger, to fly swiftly to Pluto, and bid him release Proserpina.

"But if she has eaten in Erebus even I cannot take her from Pluto," said Jupiter.

When Mercury went down into the kingdom of darkness, he took Spring with him. They flew over the River Styx and passed Cerberus. When Cerberus, his three great jaws wide open, sprang at them, Spring loosened her mantle and shook such a shower of white petals in his face that he could not see. His mouths were filled with them, and they clung to the lashes

Mercury and Spring flew over the River Styx. Some of

of his eyes. Some fell into the River Styx and floated on the dark water.

"They are like the fair queen, Proserpina, on her black marble throne," said Charon, the boatman.

"Such a dreary place to keep the daughter of Ceres!" thought Mercury, as they flew through the gloomy caverns and passages toward Pluto's palace.

Soon Pluto began to notice a faint fragrance that reminded him of the earth world above. He hurried to the doors of his palace. Proserpina felt the mild warmth and followed.

the petals fell into the river and floated on the dark water

They saw Mercury approaching, with Spring floating at his side. "Rejoice, O daughter of Ceres," said Mercury, "for Jupiter bids you return to earth, which lies brown and barren because of grief over your loss."

Pluto frowned more fiercely than ever. "She has eaten six seeds of a pomegranate," he said. "The fates decree that whoever eats in Erebus may never leave."

"But only six little seeds!" begged Proserpina. "There are twice six months in the year. Only let me see my mother! Let me feel the warm sunshine and soft winds, and gather flowers again, and I will come back to you!"

Pluto had grown to love Proserpina dearly. He could not bear to lose her forever, yet he wished her to be happy. So he agreed to let her go back to her mother for six months of the year, but the other six she promised to spend with him.

With Spring on one side and Mercury on the other, Proserpina journeyed up to earth, where Ceres awaited her.

As the ground opened to let them out, the cold winds hurried away beyond the sea. Ceres dropped her mantle of gray and laughed with joy to hold her daughter once more in her arms. The bare branches burst into bud, and tiny leaves sprang from every twig. Starry white flowers sprinkled the moss, and the perfume of Spring filled the forest.

Mercury flew back to Mount Olympus, but Spring began her journey over the earth to star the fields with blossoms and carry the tidings that Proserpina had come back.

And so, even now, when Proserpina is on earth, we have the flowers and fruits of Spring and Summer, and when she returns to Pluto, the leaves begin to fall, and then the cold, dark, windy days come, and we have Autumn and Winter.

CUPID AND PSYCHE

ONCE there lived in Greece a blue-eyed princess named Psyche. She was so fair, so beautiful, that strangers came from far-away countries to look at her and scatter roses in her path. When she smiled, even the gods were delighted as they watched her from the heights of Mount Olympus.

Only one grew angry when Psyche was praised. Venus, the goddess of Beauty, looked down at her temples on the earth and saw that they were empty. The young men who should have brought garlands for her altars were casting wreaths of roses at Psyche's feet and singing hymns of praise to her. So Venus called her son Cupid and sent him to wound Psyche with one of his golden arrows.

Cupid sharpened his arrows and fled down to the palace where Psyche lay asleep. He lightly touched one of his golden arrows to her side. At once Psyche awoke and turned her eyes toward Cupid, although she could not see him, for he was invisible.

She was so wonderfully fair that Cupid's heart beat wildly as he bent over her, and a weakness came over him such as he had never felt before. His hand slipped, and he wounded himself with his own arrow. That moment Cupid fell in love with Psyche, a human maiden.

Troubled and bewildered, he flew back to Olympus and praised the lovely Psyche to his mother. Now Venus was more angry with Psyche than before. By her arts she turned all of Psyche's lovers away from her, and she forbade Cupid ever to enter the palace of the blue-eyed princess or to look upon her again.

But Cupid loved Psyche too much to give up so easily. He decided somehow he would find a way to marry her.

Soon Psyche's older sisters were married to great princes, but no young man sought Psyche, although she grew more and more lovely. Finally her parents, feeling sure that the gods were angry, journeyed to the temple of Apollo to seek advice of the wise men there.

"The maiden is to be the bride of a god," the parents were told, "a monster of such power that neither gods nor men can resist him. He awaits her on the top of the mountain."

This answer filled the king and queen and all their people with terror, but Psyche robed herself in her most beautiful garments and, followed by her parents and friends, ascended the mountain. At the top they bade her goodby and left her there alone.

While Psyche stood on the mountain top, weeping and trembling with fright, Zephyr, the west wind, lifted her gently in his arms and carried her to a flowery valley below. Near by in a grove of tall and stately trees she saw a wonderful white palace, and in an open place fountains played amid blossoming branches. As she drew nearer to the palace she knew it was the home of a god, so great was its splendor. Golden pillars supported the high-arched roof, and paintings and sculpture ornamented the walls.

As she walked through the lovely rooms a voice full of sweetness spoke to her, "Fair Princess, all that you behold is yours. Command us, we are your servants." Filled with wonder and delight, Psyche looked about in all directions, but saw no one. The voice continued, "Here is your chamber, and your bed of down; here is your bath, and in the adjoining alcove there is food."

Psyche bathed, and put on the lovely garments prepared for her, then seated herself on a chair of carved ivory. At once there floated to its place before her a table covered with gold-

en dishes and with the finest food. Although she could see no one, invisible hands served her, and unseen musicians played on lutes and sang to her.

For a long time Psyche did not see the master of the palace. He visited her only in the night time, going away before morning dawned, but his voice was gentle and tender, not at all like that of a monster. Psyche sometimes begged him to stay through the day, but always he replied, "If you beheld my face, perhaps you would fear me, perhaps adore me, but I would rather you should love me as an equal than adore me as a god."

Psyche next begged her husband to allow her sisters to visit her. Although Cupid, for it was Cupid who was her husband, knew there would be trouble if they entered his home, he yielded to Psyche's pleading, and Zephyr was sent to bring them across the mountain and down to the enchanted valley. At first they were happy to see their young sister and to find her safe, but soon, seeing all the splendor in Psyche's palace, envy sprang up in their hearts. They questioned her rudely concerning her husband.

"Is he not some dreadful monster," they asked, "who will devour you before long? Remember what the wise men said!"

Before their visit was over they begged Psyche to look at Cupid as he lay asleep. They urged her to carry a lamp and a great knife, so that she might cut off his head if he were indeed a monster. Psyche promised to do so, and her sisters departed.

Psyche hid the lamp and knife where she could find them quickly. At midnight, when her husband was sleeping, she arose, lit her lamp, and bent over his couch. The light showed

While her husband slept, she lit her lamp and bent over his couch

her not a monster, but a youth more beautiful than any she had ever seen, with golden curls falling over his pillow, and white wings gleaming softly, like pearl and crystal.

As she turned to put out the lamp a drop of burning oil fell upon his shoulder. Cupid awoke and, looking at her sorrowfully, spread his shining wings and flew out of the window. Psyche held her arms wide and, standing on the ledge of the window, tried to follow him. But Zephyr did not receive her, and she fell.

For an instant Cupid turned back to her. "Love cannot live where there is suspicion," he said sadly, and flew away.

As Psyche lay weeping, the palace and gardens and fountains vanished, and she found herself again in her own land. Sadly she went to the palace and told her sisters what had happened. She would not stay with her sisters, but wandered away to seek her beloved. Day and night, without food or rest, she journeyed over the wildest mountains. At last she saw a beautiful temple gleaming on a hill.

"Perhaps he is there," she thought, and climbed breathlessly to the hilltop. She entered the temple. Before the altar of Ceres, the Goddess of the Crops, she saw sheaves of barley, ears of corn, piles of grain, and sickles and rakes thrown down in careless disorder by the tired harvesters.

Psyche stooped and carefully piled the grain and the sheaves of barley. She gathered the sickles and rakes and placed them on the steps of the temple, where the reapers might find them in the morning. Then, when she had swept the floor, she seated herself to rest.

Ceres, who had been watching, though Psyche could not see her, was pleased at Psyche's service, and advised her to go at once to Venus, offer to serve her, and beg for pity and for-giveness. When Psyche reached the court of Venus, she knelt before the goddess and promised to serve her in whatever way Venus might wish if only she might be allowed to see Cupid and be forever near him. Venus was still angry so she would not promise to forgive Psyche. Instead, she set her the most difficult tasks she could find.

She led Psyche to a storehouse where there were great piles of wheat, barley, millet, lentils, and beans, which Venus kept for her doves.

"First sort these grains," said Venus. "Put each kind in a separate bag, and finish the task by nightfall."

Psyche sat down on the floor of the storeroom and gazed hopelessly at the piles of grain. She knew she could not finish the task before evening, nor even in many days. But Cupid, who still loved her, had been listening, and he now sent those tireless little workers, the ants, to help. They came marching from their hills in long black lines and crawled up on the piles of grain. Then, each carrying one kernel at a time, they patiently sorted the piles and filled the bags before evening.

When Venus returned and saw that Psyche's task was completed, she was more angry than ever, for she felt sure that Cupid had helped Psyche. So she threw a piece of black bread to Psyche for her supper, and went away.

The next morning Venus sent Psyche to bring a sample of golden wool from each of the sheep in a flock that fed across a nearby river. As Psyche stood on the river bank wondering how she could cross, the river god bade the rushes and reeds murmur softly and tell her she must not try to cross in the morning, nor venture among the angry rams until the noon shadows lay deep and the sheep went to rest in the shade.

Psyche waited on the river bank until noontime, when the sheep were drowsing in the shade, and then crossed safely over. She gathered the golden fleece from the bushes where it was clinging, and carried it back to Venus. But Venus gave her no praise, only another crust for her supper.

The third day Venus commanded Psyche to go to the underworld to visit Pluto, the ruler, and his beautiful wife, Proserpina. Psyche was to say to Proserpina, "My mistress Venus begs you to send her a little of your beauty, for in caring for her wounded son she has lost some of her own."

Now Psyche was more helpless than ever, for she was sure

she never could travel on foot to Erebus, the dark place under the earth, where Proserpina and Pluto lived. But when Psyche was most downhearted a friendly voice explained to her how she might safely pass the dangers on her way.

It told her how to get Charon, the aged boatman of the River Styx, which she would have to cross, to row her across the stream and back again. The voice also told her how to charm Cerberus, the three-headed dog who guarded the gates of the underworld, so that he would let her pass. And the voice warned her especially not to open the jar in which she was to carry the precious beauty back to Venus.

The voice reminded her of Cupid, whom she had lost. It was tender, like the voice of her lover, and gentle. So courage came into her heart, and she set forth, carrying a golden jar in her hands.

When she came to the River Styx, the aged boatman took her hand gently, and led her to his boat. He ferried her across the dark water.

When Psyche reached the other side she walked through a dark cave and on through a narrow passageway, dripping with water, until she came to a wider entrance where Cerberus, with his three great heads, barked fiercely and shook the earth with his growls. Trembling, she kept her face toward him, talking quietly to him as she drew nearer.

His barking ceased, and his growling grew fainter and fainter. When she reached him he lay down and thumped the ground with his tail, just as the friendly dogs of the earth always did when Psyche passed by them.

So Psyche continued on her way to Proserpina's throne, where she delivered the message from Venus. When Proser-

Psyche, carrying the golden jar, crossed the river with Charon

pina had filled the golden jar, Psyche returned as she had come, passing the dreadful Cerberus, and going again through the cave. Then she crossed the river with Charon, who had waited for her. At last she found herself in the sunshine, near a grassy bank. As she sat down to rest, she looked longingly at the little jar.

"What harm can it do," Psyche thought, "if I just peep in and take a little bit of the beauty for myself, so that when Cupid again sees me I shall be even more lovely?"

So she took off the lid, and at once up into her face flew clouds of strange fragrance. She could not see the jar or even the grass around her, but quickly fell asleep. Cupid, still invisible, had been waiting and watching at the entrance of the cavern for her return. He flew to her side, and, gathering the clouds of sleepy magic, he placed them again in the jar and wakened Psyche.

"Again," he said, "you have almost perished because of your curiosity."

Psyche was so happy to be with Cupid that she would have forgotten to finish her errand. But Cupid knew that Venus must be obeyed, and he sent Psyche on with the jar while he himself flew to Jupiter and begged that Psyche might be made immortal so that she might stay with him forever.

Jupiter granted Cupid's plea, and sent Mercury, messenger of the gods, to carry Psyche to Mount Olympus, where the gods were waiting to welcome her.

A glorious haze of light, as many-colored as a rainbow, hid the throne of Jupiter from Psyche's sight, for being still mortal she was not permitted to look at the ruler of the gods.

Hebe, the cupbearer of the immortals, advanced to meet

her, carrying in her hand a goblet of nectar, which she gave to Psyche. The fragrant liquid not only refreshed Psyche but bestowed upon her the gift of immortality. Immediately after she had emptied the goblet her weariness fell from her, her body felt new strength, her heart was filled with new gladness, and her face and form appeared more lovely than ever.

The haze of light rolled away from Jupiter's throne, and Psyche beheld the ruler of the gods. Kneeling before him, she gave him humble thanks.

Venus, feeling forgiveness in her heart, now came forward to embrace Psyche and give her to Cupid for his bride.

Ever after, on the sunny summit of Mount Olympus Cupid and Psyche lived together in happiness.

PHAETON AND THE CHARIOT OF THE SUN

O NCE, on their way from school, two Greek boys began to
quarrel.

"You are nobody!" said one. "Who is your father?"

"My father is Phoebus Apollo, God of the Sun," said the
other. He drives the four great horses of the day. He lights the
earth and the heavens with his light, and I am his son."

His comrade laughed loudly at his boast. He could not believe that the father of Phaeton, his schoolmate, was Apollo,
the god of the sun. So he called the other boys together and
told them Phaeton's story. They all laughed at Phaeton and
made fun of him for pretending to be the son of a god.

The boy, his cheeks flaming with anger, ran home and
burst into his mother's room. He told her what had happened.

"Is Apollo indeed my father?" he demanded. "How can I
be sure, how can I find proof?"

Clymene, the sea nymph, his mother, smiled and drew
him to her side. She told him again of the glories of Apollo,
as she had often told him before.

"Soon," she said, "you will wish to go yourself to the land
where the sun rises and find him where he sits on his throne

of light, with the four seasons beside him and the hours and the days grouped near by. Why not journey there and see for yourself, and find proof that Apollo is your father?"

So, although Clymene grieved to have him leave her, she made him ready for the journey and bade him a loving farewell.

Phaeton traveled many days through gray and barren lands, over mountains and across streams, until at last he reached the land of the rising sun and saw afar off the flaming light which glowed about the palace of his father.

As he drew nearer he saw that the columns of the palace were of gold and ivory, upholding a jeweled roof. The steps leading to the entrance shone with every kind of precious stone. But he hardly paused to look at all this splendor, so anxious was he to see his father.

Phaeton entered the palace and there on his golden throne in the great central hall, surrounded by a wonderful white light, he saw Apollo, clad in pale purple, beautiful and dazzling.

On the sun god's left stood Spring, her head crowned with flowers, and Summer, with poppies in her hair. On his right stood Autumn, wreathed in grapes, and aged Winter bowed over with the weight of ice and snow.

Apollo looked down and saw the boy as he drew near, his hand shielding his eyes. He knew in a moment that this was his son Phaeton, and laid aside the rays that shone about his head, so that Phaeton might not be blinded by their brightness.

"O light of the boundless world, Phoebus, my father!" Phaeton cried. "If you are indeed my parent, give me some proof by which I may be known as your son."

Apollo stretched out his hand to Phaeton and drew him nearer. He looked at him, so straight and brave and young, and the sun god was proud of him.

"My son," he said, "for proof, ask of me what you wish and it shall be given."

Phaeton at once thought of the chariot of the sun. He pictured himself riding across the sky holding the reins of his father's horses. He imagined the amazement of his friends if they could see him.

"Let me for one day drive the chariot of the sun," he answered. "Let me ride from morning until evening through the clouds in your chariot, holding the reins of your four horses."

Apollo sat on his golden throne. On his left stood Spring

Apollo was sorry that he had made Phaeton so rash a
promise, and begged him to choose something else. He reminded the boy that he was not yet grown, and that he was
only mortal. He told of the dreadful dangers that every day
surrounded the chariot on its upward and downward path.

"The first part of the way," he said, "is so steep that the
horses can barely climb it, and the last part descends so rapidly that I can hardly hold them. Besides, the heaven itself is
always turning, hurrying the stars with it, and always I am

and Summer; on his right stood Autumn and aged Winter

afraid that it will sweep me from the chariot and carry the horses from the road. The way leads through the abode of the frightful monsters. You must pass the horns of the Bull, the Lion's jaws, the Scorpion, and the Crab.

"O Phaeton," he begged, "look around the world and choose whatever you wish that is precious, whether in the sea or in the midst of the earth, and it shall be yours; but give up this longing to drive my chariot, which can mean only death to you."

"No," said Phaeton, "I do not care for anything either in the sea or on the earth. I want only to drive the chariot of Phoebus, my father."

So Phoebus Apollo sadly led the way to the chariot. It was of gold, with a seat of jewels, and around it flamed such a blaze of light that for a moment Phaeton was afraid to go nearer, it seemed so fiery and scorching.

Rosy-fingered Dawn threw open the silver doors of the east, and there before him Phaeton saw the stars fading away, and the moon, her nightly journey finished, hurrying from the sky. The four great chargers were led from their stalls, and Phaeton cried out in delight as he saw their arched necks and stamping feet. Fire poured from their nostrils, and their hoofs were shod with light.

Phoebus bathed the boy's face with a powerful oil so that he would not be burned, set the rays of the sun on his head, and bade him hold tight to the reins, keep to the middle of the road, and follow the tracks of the wheels.

"Do not go too high," he warned, "or you will burn the heavenly dwellings; nor too low, or you will set the earth on fire."

Phaeton joyfully grasped the reins and, holding his head high with delight and pride, rode into the purple path of the morning sky.

The horses darted forward with mighty strength and scattered the clouds. Soon they felt that the touch on the reins was not their master's, but a lighter one, and that the chariot itself was not so heavy. So, filling the air with their fiery snorting, they sped on faster and faster, while Phaeton tried to hold them back.

Phaeton fell headlong, like a streak of lightning, into the river

They left the traveled road and dashed headlong in among the stars. Phaeton was borne along like the petal of a flower by the wind, and did not know how to guide his fiery steeds. Looking down, he saw the earth spreading below, and his knees grew weak with fright. He wished that he had never left his mother or asked to drive the chariot of the sun.

Around him on every side were the monsters of the sky. The Scorpion reached his great claws toward the chariot as it passed, and Phaeton dropped the reins. The horses galloped off into unknown regions of the sky, now high up toward the abode of the gods, now downward, so close to the earth that the mountains caught fire, the Alps covered with snow grew hot, and the Apennines flamed.

The earth cracked open. Grassy plains were scorched into deserts. Even the sea shrank, and the fishes and water nymphs hurried down to the deepest parts of the ocean.

So terrible was the heat that Mother Earth cried out to Jupiter, "O ruler of the gods, I can no more supply fruits for men, or food for cattle, and my brother Ocean suffers with me. Your own heaven is smoking, and your clouds are on fire. Oh, take thought for our deliverance!"

Then Jupiter mounted the tower on Olympus, from which he shook his thunderbolts and his forked lightning. He hurled a mighty bolt at the chariot and poured rain on the smoking earth until the fires were extinguished.

Poor Phaeton, still clinging to the reeling chariot as it swayed across the sky, was struck by Jupiter's thunderbolt and, his hair on fire, fell headlong like a streak of lightning into the River Eridanus, which soothed him and cooled his burning body.

ARCAS AND CALLISTO

THERE was once in peaceful Arcady, in Greece, a fair and gentle nymph named Callisto. The gods had given her many graces and blessings, the greatest of which was her little son, Arcas.

Jupiter, chief of the gods, was so pleased with Callisto's goodness and charm that he came often to visit her and watch her at play with Arcas.

These visits filled the jealous Juno, wife of Jupiter, with anger, and she planned a cruel punishment for Callisto. Wrapping herself in her long gray cloak, the goddess descended from Mount Olympus, passing through the dusky cloud gates down to the earth. She found Callisto just awakening in her forest bower. Her rosy little son, Arcas, lay asleep beside her.

Juno made herself invisible and waited until Callisto rose and came out of her retreat. Then, touching the nymph on her shoulder, Juno changed her into a great furry bear.

Poor Callisto saw her slender white fingers change into long claws and her arms grow black and hairy. She fell to the earth and began to walk on all fours. Then Juno returned to Mount Olympus.

When the other nymphs came to seek Callisto, they could not find her. Only a great hairy bear stood in the entrance to the bower, trying to fondle the little boy, Arcas, and turn him over with her paw as he lay asleep.

The nymphs drove the bear away, although it looked back at them sadly as they flung sticks and stones after it.

Thinking that the bear had killed Callisto, the maidens took Arcas to a shepherd, who loved and cared for him.

Sometimes the shepherd saw a bear prowling around his hut, trying to look in at the window or the door. He drove the beast away and flung his spear at it, until at last the poor thing was afraid to come near the hut, and stayed at the edge of the woods, watching always for a sight of the little boy who lived with the shepherd.

Sometimes Arcas would stray near the forest, gathering flowers or playing with his ball. Then the bear would run to greet him, growling softly and kindly, but the child always screamed and ran back.

When Arcas grew old enough, the shepherd taught him to use a spear and took him hunting.

As long as the shepherd was with Arcas, Callisto hid herself. But one day the youth came alone, holding his spear in his hand and feeling very brave and proud.

Callisto stood on her hind legs and came toward him, holding out her great paws, trying to speak and tell him that she was his mother, enchanted into this wild beast. Arcas saw her coming and raised his spear to kill the bear, but something held his arm and the spear was not thrown.

Jupiter, watching over Arcas on his first hunt, had seen beneath the bear's fur and hairy paws, and knew that this was the nymph Callisto.

Arcas raised his spear to kill the bear, but something held his arm

He stayed the hand of Arcas, and took away his spear. He could not undo Juno's evil work, so he changed Arcas into a young bear. At once he understood his mother and knew what she had been trying to tell him.

Callisto and Arcas would have been happy to roam the woods together, but Jupiter thought of something better for them. He took them up into the heavenly realms and gave them the sky for their playground, and you can see them there on clear nights, the Great Bear and the Little Bear.

Juno was angry when she saw the new constellations placed among the stars, but she could not interfere because Jupiter was the ruler of the heavens.

So she went to Neptune, the god who ruled the sea, and made him promise her that he would forbid the bears to rest beneath the ocean as the other stars do during the day.

And so the Big Bear and the Little Bear, always moving around near the Pole, stay forever in the sky, though you can see them only at night. Being near each other they are happy, and have learned to rest content among the clouds.

ATALANTA AND HIPPOMENES

ATALANTA was a Greek maiden who could run faster than any one on earth. She could outrun the winds, Boreas, the north wind, and Zephyr, the west wind. Only Mercury, the messenger of the gods, with his winged sandals, ran more swiftly.

Besides being so fleet-footed, Atalanta was very beautiful, and many Greek youths from every part of the kingdom wished to marry her. But Atalanta did not wish to marry any one and turned them all away, saying, "I shall be the bride only of him who shall outrun me in the race, but death must be the penalty of all who try and fail."

In spite of this hard condition there were a few brave suitors willing to risk their lives for a chance of winning Atalanta.

For one of the races the runners chose the youth Hippomenes for judge.

Hippomenes felt both pity and scorn for the runners. He thought they were foolish to risk their lives, and told them to go home. He reminded them that the land was full of lovely maidens who were kinder and more gentle than Atalanta.

"But you have not yet seen Atalanta," said one of the suitors to Hippomenes. "You do not know all her beauty and loveliness. See, here she comes!"

Hippomenes looked, and saw Atalanta as she drew near. She laid aside her cloak and made ready for the race. For a moment she stood poised like a graceful white bird about to fly.

The suitors who stood beside her trembled with fear and eagerness.

At a word from Hippomenes the runners were off, but at the first step Atalanta flew ahead. Her tunic fluttered behind her like a banner. Her hair, loosened from its ribbon, blew about her shoulders in bright waves.

As she ran, Hippomenes thought her very beautiful and became envious of the runner who might win her. He shouted praises when she reached the goal far ahead of her poor suitors.

Hippomenes forgot that the penalty of failure was death. He did not remember the advice he had given the other runners to go home and forget the loveliness of Atalanta. He knew only that he loved her and must himself race with her.

Raising his head toward Mount Olympus, he prayed to Venus, the Goddess of Love, and asked her to help him.

As he stood beside Atalanta, waiting the signal for the race to start, Venus appeared to him and slipped three golden apples into his hands.

"Throw them one by one in Atalanta's path," whispered Venus.

The goddess was invisible to everyone but Hippomenes. No one saw her as she gave him the apples, nor heard her as she told him what to do with them.

Atalanta looked pityingly at the handsome youth as he

Just before Atalanta reached the goal, he threw the third apple

stood ready to run. She was sorry for him, and for a moment she hesitated and almost wished that he might win the race.

The signal was given, and Atalanta and Hippomenes flew swiftly over the sand. Atalanta was soon ahead, but Hippomenes, sending up a prayer to Venus, tossed one of his golden apples so that it fell directly in front of Atalanta.

Astonished at the beautiful apple which seemed to have fallen from nowhere, she stooped to pick it up.

That instant Hippomenes passed her, but Atalanta holding the apple firmly in her hand, at once darted ahead. Again she outdistanced Hippomenes. Then he threw the second apple.

Atalanta could not pass without picking it up, and then, because of the apple in her other hand, paused a moment longer. When she looked up, Hippomenes was far ahead.

But soon Atalanta gained on him, then overtook and passed him. Then, just before she reached the goal, Hippomenes threw the third apple.

"I can win easily," though Atalanta, "even though I stoop for this other apple." As she was already holding an apple in each hand, she paused just for an instant as she wondered how to grasp the third.

That moment Hippomenes shot past, reaching the goal before Atalanta.

Amid the wild shouts of those who watched, he wrapped the maiden's cloak around her shoulders and led her away. Hippomenes was so happy that he forgot to thank the goddess Venus, who followed them to the marriage feast.

Invisible, she moved among the wedding guests. She saw Atalanta place the golden apples in a bowl of ivory and admire their beauty, but Hippomenes, in his delight, thought no more of the apples or of the goddess who had given them to him.

Venus was angry with Hippomenes for being so thoughtless, and instead of blessing the lovers she caused them to be changed into a lion and a lioness, doomed forever to draw the chariot of Cybele, the mother of Jupiter, through the heavens and over the earth.

JASON AND THE GOLDEN FLEECE

THERE was once a young prince named Jason. His parents ruled over Iolcus, in Thessaly. Their kingdom was filled with happiness and peace, for they were wise and good and noble.

But one day the king's brother, Pelias, came riding at the head of an army. He made war on Iolcus, and took the kingdom from Jason's father. Pelias had evil in his heart, and would have killed his brother and Prince Jason, but they fled and hid themselves among lowly people who loved them.

There was at this time a strange and wonderful school in the mountains of Thessaly, a school where the princes of Greece were taught and made strong of body and brave of heart.

Chiron, the centaur, half man, half horse, kept this school and reared the young princes. He taught them how to hunt and to fight and to sing, how to take care of their bodies and to bear themselves according to their birth.

So Jason, being still a little boy, was sent to this wonderful school. Here he grew up with the other Greek princes of his age.

At last came the time when Chiron told him the story of the evil King Pelias, who had stolen the kingdom of Iolcus and had driven Jason's father from his throne.

Jason was brown and strong and hardened by Chiron's training. He girded on his sword and set out to take the kingdom away from Pelias. It was early in spring, and as he journeyed he came to a swollen stream and saw an aged woman gazing in despair at the waters she could not cross.

Jason remembered his training as a prince, and offered to carry her across. He lifted her to his back, and she gave him her staff for support. He stepped into the swift-running stream, which no one else had dared cross, and although he bent under

the weight of his burden he fought bravely against the waters with all his strength, but in crossing the stream he lost one of his sandals.

At last he reached the opposite bank and set the old woman on the grass. Suddenly, in a flash of light, she was transformed into the glorious figure of Juno, queen of the gods. At her feet stood a peacock. Its purple and blue and green tail feathers swept over the grass and its shining head rested against her hand.

The goddess promised aid and protection to Jason forever after, and vanished as quickly as she had appeared. So in all his undertakings Jason was watched over and blessed by Juno in return for his kindness to her.

When Jason reached Iolcus he saw many people in the marketplace, because it was a feast day. Jason was a handsome young man, and the people gathered around him in admiration.

But King Pelias, who was among the people, looked first at his feet. He always looked first at the feet of any stranger because, years before, he had been told by an oracle to beware of a man with only one sandal.

When Pelias saw that Jason was wearing only one sandal, his face became deathly pale.

"Who are you?" asked the king of Jason.

"I am Jason, and I have come to demand my father's throne."

The king pretended that he was happy to see his nephew, took him to the palace, arranged for a banquet to be given in his honor, and entertained him royally. But all the while, Pelias was planning Jason's death.

While they ate, the bards gathered around the hall and sang of heroes and brave deeds, as bards were accustomed to sing at banquets of kings.

They sang of the story of Phrixus and Helle, the two Greek children who escaped their wicked stepmother, riding on the back of Mercury's golden-fleeced ram. They sang of how Nephele, the real mother, weeping and heavy of heart, placed her little son and daughter on the ram's back and watched them as they sped away from Thessaly. The ram leapt into the air and flew through the clouds as if he had wings. They passed over the sea toward Colchis, the kingdom of their uncle, where they knew they would be safe.

The bards touched their lute strings sadly, and sang of how little Helle became frightened, as she looked down upon the tossing sea, and how she fell from the ram's back into the water, which ever after was called Hellespont.

But Phrixus clung fast and reached Colchis in safety. He

offered the ram as a thank-offering to the gods, and hung the Golden Fleece high on an oak tree, setting a fearful dragon to guard it.

Here, after all the years, it still hung, waiting for some young hero to come and conquer and claim it.

The bards sang of the glory of the Fleece, of its glittering richness, and of the heroes who had died seeking it. Pelias noticed how Jason's eyes were shining. He knew that the song had moved him and rightly guessed that Jason longed to go in search of this Golden Fleece.

Pelias thought that this would be a good way to bring about Jason's death. The dragon had killed many other youths who had been rash enough to seek the Golden Fleece, and Pelias felt certain that Jason would perish also. So he leaned toward the young prince and urged him to set out on the adventure and bring back the Fleece which rightfully belonged to Thessaly.

Jason sprang from his seat and vowed that he would go.

First he visited Juno's temple and asked help on his journey. She gave him the limb of a mighty and wonderful oak for the figurehead of his boat, which would speak to him in time of danger, and advise and warn him on his voyage.

Then Juno bade Minerva provide a swift-sailing vessel, made from the wood of pine trees which grew on Mount Pelion.

Jason called his vessel the Argo, and sent for the young princes of Chiron's school to come with him and help in the search for the Golden Fleece.

Hercules came and also Admetus, Theseus, Orpheus, Castor, and Pollux, all the bravest and noblest heroes of

Greece, anxious to take part in this adventure and to bring the Golden Fleece back to Thessaly.

Juno sped them on their way with favorable winds, and the Argo sailed swiftly toward Colchis. When danger threatened, the branch of the talking oak spoke wise words of help and counsel. It guided them safely between the clashing rocks of the Symplegades, and past the land of the cruel Harpies. So they came at last, after many adventures, to Colchis, the kingdom of Eetes.

Now the Fleece had hung for so long in his realm that King Eetes was unwilling to part with it. Like Pelias, he was

crafty and full of wiles, and did not refuse Jason, but agreed
to give him the Fleece on certain conditions.

First Jason must catch and harness two wild, fire-breath-
ing bulls; then plough a stony field, sacred to Mars. After that
he must sow the field with dragon's teeth and conquer the
host of armed men which would grow from them. Last of all,
he must overcome the dragon which coiled around the foot of
the oak and guarded the Fleece.

Jason feared that these tasks were impossible for any mortal to fulfil without the help of the gods. So he hurried down
to the vessel to speak with the branch of the talking oak. On
his way he met Medea, the princess of Colchis. She was young
and beautiful and skilled in all manner of enchantments and
magic. Her heart was filled with kindness toward the brave
young stranger and she wished to help him.

Jason caught the fiery bulls, harnessed them, drove them

She gave Jason her strongest charms and her wisest counsel. By the aid of Medea's magic he caught the fiery bulls as they came roaring from their pasture. He harnessed them and drove them over the stony field, and made them drag the heavy plough which turned the earth in dark furrows.

Eetes was amazed, for no one had ever yoked or harnessed these bulls before.

When the field was ready, Jason asked for the dragon's teeth, and Eetes gave them to him in a helmet. Up and down the long furrows he sowed them, and when the last one was in the ground, he ploughed the earth again, and covered them and waited.

Long rows of shining spears began to pierce the ground and to shoot up into the air. Then rose the plumed helmets of a thousand soldiers; then their shields, and their bodies.

over the stony field, and made them drag the heavy plough

They stood, full armed and fierce, looking over the field. When they beheld Jason, they ran toward him with waving spears and a clatter of shields.

From his pocket Jason took a magic stone which Medea had given him. He threw it into the midst of the thousand soldiers; it fell among them like discord itself. Each soldier thought another had thrown it, and each man began to fight his neighbor. More and more furiously they fought. Soon the ploughed field was covered with fallen soldiers. They continued to kill one another until not one was left.

Then Medea led Jason to the sacred grove where the dragon watched beside the Fleece. The huge monster rose up, roaring terribly, as Jason approached. He breathed clouds of smoke and fire and lashed his tail against the oak tree.

Jason bravely advanced until he was so near that he could feel the heat of the flames that poured from the dragon's throat. Then he took a magic liquid, which Medea had given him, and threw it straight into the face of the dragon. In a moment the monster fell back to the earth, and coiling himself lazily on the grass, went to sleep.

Jason climbed the tree and brought down the wonderful glittering Fleece, then hurried back to his ship.

King Eetes knew that Jason could not have accomplished these things without the aid of his daughter Medea and he was very angry, and plotted revenge against both Jason and Medea.

But the young people had fallen in love and Jason planned to take Medea as his bride to Thessaly. He smuggled her onto his ship and they sailed away under cover of night.

When Jason returned to Iolcus with the Golden Fleece, he did not get his father's throne after all. Medea used her magic

Jason took a magic fluid and threw it at the dragon's face

powers to kill Pelias but, even so, Pelias's son forced them to leave, and go to Corinth.

Medea loved Jason very deeply and was happy with him and their two sons, even though she lived in a strange land and could never return home because of her father's anger. But Jason was not as faithful and loyal as Medea. He grew tired of her and fell in love with the young daughter of Creon, King of Corinth.

Jason still had a burning desire to be a king and knew that if he married Creon's daughter he would one day inherit the throne. So, without Medea's knowledge, he wooed the young Glauce. And it was not until all the plans for the wedding were made that he told Medea he planned to leave her.

Medea thought of the love she had given Jason and of the crimes she had committed for him, and, suddenly, all her love turned to hate. She decided that she would have to make Jason pay for his faithlessness.

Pretending that she had accepted her fate, she sent her two children to deliver a beautiful robe to Jason's bride-to-be. Medea had covered the robe with poison. When Glauce started to put it on, flames burst from it, and soon the bride was dead.

Jason came hurrying to Medea, broken-hearted, to save his sons, because he thought Creon's relatives might seek to harm them, in revenge.

But by this time Medea, in her great sorrow, had become insane and had murdered her two sons in order to punish Jason even more. She would not even let Jason bury them but did it herself and then, using her magic powers, she summoned a chariot and some dragons and they took her up in the sky and flew her away from Corinth—we don't know where.

PERSEUS AND ANDROMEDA

A fisherman was tending his nets one morning on the coast of the island of Serifos when he noticed something floating far out on the water. He rowed out and found a great wooden chest, which he towed to shore. When the fisherman pried up the heavy cover, he found inside the chest a beautiful woman with a little baby clasped in her arms.

She had been shut in the chest for so many hours, floating over the sea, that she was too weak to stand. So the fisherman lifted both baby and mother in his arms and carried them to his home, because he and his wife had no children of their own.

When the mother had eaten and felt refreshed, she told the fisherman that her name was Princess Danae and that her baby was Perseus, the little son of Jupiter. She told him that her father, King Acrisius of Argos, had shut them in the chest and set them afloat on the sea because he had heard from an oracle that some day the baby Perseus would grow up and cause his death.

The fisherman and his wife took good care of Danae and Perseus, until Perseus had become a fine young man.

Even though her son was now grown, Danae was still

beautiful, and when King Polydectes of Serifos saw her, he fell in love with her and married her. But Polydectes did not like Perseus, because the king did not want Danae to love anyone but him.

So, one day, Polydectes told Perseus he thought it was time for him to go off on some adventures and make a name for himself. This pleased Perseus because he did not realize how dangerous the journey was on which Polydectes was sending him.

The king sent Perseus to cut off the head of Medusa, one of three terrible monsters, called gorgons, who lived far away in the wilderness. These horrible creatures had snakes instead of hair, and everyone who looked at them was turned into stone.

Perseus did not know where Medusa lived and wandered from place to place for many months.

Minerva, the goddess who watches over heroes, saw that Perseus was getting tired and discouraged. She knew that he could not succeed in his quest without the help of the gods. Although Perseus wore a sword and carried a shield and his sandals were light and strong, Minerva knew that he would need weapons and armor more powerful than mortal sword or shield, and sandals swifter than his leather ones.

Therefore she called upon Mercury, who brought his winged sandals of silver. Pluto, God of Erebus, loaned his plumed helmet, which would make the wearer invisible. Minerva herself gave her shield, which nothing could pierce or shatter. Then Mercury told Perseus that he could not direct him to the gorgons, but he could tell him where to find the

Gray Ladies. These Gray Ladies could tell Perseus where to find Medusa.

"And will they?" asked Perseus.

"If you do just what I tell you to," said Mercury, "they will be forced to help you."

Then Perseus strapped the winged sandals on his feet and felt himself rise with a strange lightness. When the helmet touched his head, he became invisible. With the strong and beautiful shield in his hand he set out, as swiftly as Mercury himself, flying through the air over tree tops and temples, toward the cavern of the three old women, the Gray Ladies.

As he drew near their cavern, he could hear them singing a mournful song, and, as he peered into the gloomy depths, he saw them rocking back and forth as they sang. They were bent and wrinkled and blind, except for one movable eye which they shared among them. They passed it back and forth as each took her turn at seeing. Their long white hair hung wild and loose on their shoulders.

As Perseus watched, one of them plucked the eye from her forehead and passed it to the sister next to her. For a moment she groped, reaching out for her sister's hand. Instantly, when all three of them were in darkness, Perseus sprang into the cavern and snatched the eye as it passed between their fingers, just as Mercury had told him to do.

For a moment there was terrible confusion, for each sister thought one of the others was hiding it. Then Perseus spoke to them and they knew that a stranger had stolen their eye. They stumbled around the cavern, blindly holding out their hands to find him, wailing and pleading all the time.

Perseus was sorry for them, but he did not intend to return their eye until they told him where to find the gorgons. The Gray Ladies were willing to do anything to have their eye again, and so they agreed to give Perseus all the help they could. They told him exactly in which direction he must go, and just how to find the cavern of Medusa.

Perseus returned their eye and thanked them. Then, swiftly, he flew to the home of Medusa.

As he drew near, he saw, all around him, men and animals who had turned into stone from looking at the gorgons.

They wore such expressions of terror that Perseus was careful to keep his face turned away from the cavern, lest he should see Medusa.

From inside the cave he could hear strange noises, as if someone were walking about and complaining. He heard the whispering sound made by the hissing of the serpents that formed Medusa's hair.

Perseus hid behind one of the stone images to wait until nightfall; then he stole up quietly and found the spot where Medusa slept. Although he kept his head turned aside, he could see her reflection in the brightness of his shield.

Bending over, Perseus cut off the Gorgon's head, and carrying it with him hurried to the entrance of the cave. He rose into the air, and flew over the sea and over Africa. As he passed, some drops of the Gorgon's blood fell on the sands of the African desert and immediately changed into poisonous serpents.

At last Perseus came to the realm of a king named Atlas. When he asked for food and rest, Atlas refused him and drove him from the palace doors.

Perseus uncovered the head of Medusa and raised it in front of Atlas. As soon as the king beheld it, he was turned to stone. As Perseus watched, Atlas grew larger and larger. His hips formed the slopes of a mighty mountain; his hair and beard became forests, and thrusting his head high among the stars, he was forced to receive the weight of the sky on his shoulders. Forever after he was doomed to bear the burden.

Perseus flew on until he came to the land of Ethiopia. Here he noticed a group of people on the shore, wringing their hands and weeping. Chained to a nearby rock he saw a maiden who kept her face turned toward the sea. She seemed to be expecting something to approach from across the water.

Perseus floated down and, as he came near her, he found that she was the loveliest maiden he had ever beheld. He took off his invisible helmet and spoke to her thus:

"O Virgin, undeserving of those chains, tell me, I beseech you, your name and the name of your country, and why you are thus bound."

Replying, the maiden told Perseus that she was Andromeda, Princess of Ethiopia. She was bound to the rock to await the coming of a sea-dragon that would devour her because the gods of the sea were angry with her mother.

Being beautiful and proud of her charms, the Queen of Ethiopia had boasted that she was lovelier than the sea

At last the dragon lay still, partly in the water, partly on shore

nymphs. Neptune's daughters were angry at this boast, and as a punishment they sent a dreadful sea-dragon to carry off the fairest youths and maidens that lived in the land.

At last the king and queen were warned by the gods that they must chain their own daughter to a rock so that the dragon might be given the loveliest maiden in all the kingdom. Then, said the oracle, the dragon would be satisfied and would return to the depths of the sea from which he had come.

Even as Andromeda was telling these things to Perseus they heard a roaring sound that came from the sea. As they looked up a huge green monster swam swiftly across the water, throwing great fountains of spray toward the heavens.

Perseus sprang into the air. As the dragon came near, he darted downward like an eagle and buried his sword in the serpent's shoulder. Such a fight followed that Andromeda covered her eyes in terror.

The monster lashed his tail to the right and to the left, and in his fury split great rocks. Again and again Perseus rose into the air and swooped down upon him, wounding him until at last he lay still, partly in the water and partly on shore, his head and body stretched on the rocks and the sand, his tail floating far out on the sea.

Perseus unbound the princess, and the king and queen gave a great banquet in his honor. Then they allowed him to marry Andromeda and carry her back to his own land.

But when Perseus returned with his bride, he found that Polydectes still hated him, for Perseus knew now that the king had sent him on the dreadful journey hoping that he would not return.

Polydectes would not believe that Perseus had killed Medusa, and treated him so badly that Perseus could bear it no longer.

"I will prove to you that I do, indeed, have Medusa's head," said Perseus. And he showed the gorgon's head to Polydectes who was, of course, immediately turned to stone.

Now that Perseus no longer had enemies, he did not need or want such a horrible weapon and so he gave it to Minerva.

Danae now urged her son and his wife to take her back to her home. She longed to see her father again and to tell him that she had forgiven him. So the three of them set sail for Greece.

When they came to their homeland, they found that King Acrisius was away, attending a festival of games. When Perseus heard about the games, he decided to go and take part in them.

When his turn came to throw the discus, Perseus accidentally threw it in such a way that it went off to one side. It flew off the playing field and killed one of the spectators. The man who was killed was King Acrisius. So in spite of his efforts to avoid death by cruelly sending his daughter Danae and her baby son to sea in a locked chest, King Acrisius was killed as the oracle had said he would be—by the hand of his grandson Perseus.

ORPHEUS AND EURYDICE

ONCE on a spring morning, Orpheus, son of Apollo, sat on a hilltop high above the world, singing and playing his lyre. He sang of the spring flowers and the south wind in the trees. He made rippling melodies that sounded like the waters of fountains and tiny streams. But above all these he sang of Eurydice and his love for her.

As he played, the tall treetops bowed their heads to listen, and daffodils raised their budded stems and opened wide to hear him.

Pan and all the satyrs came running and leaping through the woods. The centaurs, who were half man and half horse, smiled to hear the music. They thought such things as mortals do in spring time, although their four feet tingled with the happiness which horses feel when they gallop over the green grass in April.

The nymphs wakened in wooded bowers and, fastening their tunics on their shoulders, hurried out to listen.

Eurydice herself opened her eyes and thought sweetly, "It is Orpheus." She dressed, twined a garland in her hair, and then ran toward the hilltop where he sang.

132

From all sides came birds and nymphs, fauns and dryads, all hurrying toward Orpheus. Little spotted snakes crawled up from their homes in the ground and wriggled through the grass. The tiny orange-colored serpent, whose bite means death, rose also and lifted his head to listen.

Now Aristaeus, the keeper of the bees, came running. His garden lay far away from the hill, but he had heard the faint echo of Orpheus's lyre.

He saw Eurydice and called to her to wait for him, but she ran on. Aristaeus tried to overtake her, but Eurydice ran more rapidly than ever. She did not want to talk to Aristaeus, but cared only to find Orpheus and sit beside him as he played.

She turned back to look at Aristaeus as he followed. At that moment she set her foot on the poisonous serpent that wriggled across her path. A fiery tongue darted out and struck Eurydice's heel, and she fell to the grass.

As Aristaeus drew nearer, he saw that the earth had opened. He saw the River Styx, and heard the far-off barking of Cerberus. He saw Charon, the hoary boatman, waiting to row Eurydice across.

Eurydice floated away. Still looking back toward the hill where Orpheus played, she put her hand in Charon's and disappeared across the dark water into the realm of Erebus.

On the hilltop Orpheus sang and watched for Eurydice, wondering why she did not come. Every other nymph and dryad, and indeed all the living things of the forest, had gathered to listen, except Eurydice, his beloved. Then he saw Aristaeus come stumbling and weeping up the hillside.

"Eurydice is dead," said Aristaeus, "and gone with Charon across the river."

"Then I will follow," said Orpheus.

He touched his lyre, and at the sound of his music sadness swept over the earth. The centaurs wept and walked away. The animals of the forest slunk back to their dens. The nymphs and dryads threw themselves on the grass and mourned. The rocks shed tears, and the earth, hearing the sad music, opened the same crevice through which Eurydice had passed and allowed Orpheus to follow.

At the sound of his lyre, Charon came ferrying back over the water and rowed Orpheus across to the land of the shades. Cerberus ceased his barking and lay down as Orpheus passed.

Through the long avenues under the earth and through

Passing through crowds of ghosts, Orpheus came to the

the great caverns of Erebus he wandered, seeking Eurydice and playing on his lyre. Never before had such sounds stolen through the quiet kingdom of Pluto. The shades of death forgot their drowsy sadness and came thronging to hear. Again they remembered the earth, and the sunshine and rain, and the sadness of loving.

Passing through crowds of ghosts, Orpheus came to the throne of Pluto and Proserpina, and sang of his sorrow:

"O gods of the underworld, to whom all who live must come, hear my words. I am Orpheus, son of Apollo, and I seek my beloved, Eurydice. Let me lead her to the earth, or I myself will remain here, for I cannot return alone."

throne of Pluto and Proserpina, and sang of his sorrow

As his fingers strayed over the lyre strings, such sorrowful music spread through Erebus that the shades began to weep. The daughters of Danaus rested from their task of drawing water in a sieve. Tantalus, who was doomed to eternal thirst, for a moment forgot his misery and listened to the song of Orpheus. For the first time, the cheeks of the Furies were wet with tears.

Proserpina's heart was filled with pity, and Pluto himself could not resist Orpheus's prayer. They sent for Eurydice, who was in a distant cavern with the newly arrived shades.

Past the dark lakes and under arches of hanging crystals she came, trying to find her way toward the music that she heard from far off.

Orpheus was allowed to take her away with him, but Pluto warned him that he must not look at her or speak to her until they reached the upper air. So Orpheus went ahead, and Eurydice followed close behind him.

Through dark passages and by the shores of many lakes they hurried without a word, until they reached the banks of the River Styx. Here the aged boatman ferried them across. Now they ran more swiftly than before in their eagerness to reach the open air.

When they had come nearly to the entrance, Orpheus felt a terrible fear that Eurydice might not be following. Forgetting the warning of Pluto, he turned and saw her lovely face smiling at him. Then, instantly, with a cry of farewell, Eurydice was borne away.

Their arms reached toward each other, but embraced only the empty air. Orpheus could hear the faint sweet call of her voice as she vanished forever into the depths of Erebus.

Orpheus went ahead, and Eurydice followed close behind

He would have turned back and followed her, but Charon would not row him across the Styx.

For seven whole days Orpheus waited, pleading with Charon, but the grim boatman still refused. Though Orpheus played on his lyre, and moved oaks and mountains with the power of his music, he could not prevail upon the gods of Erebus again, nor could he enter the dark kingdom a second time.

The rest of his life he lived in sadness and loneliness, only waiting for the time when he might die and join Eurydice.

At last death came to Orpheus. Charon ferried him across the River Styx to where Eurydice awaited him. And then they were never separated again, but hand in hand roamed forever through the shadowy land of Erebus.

THE GOLDEN TOUCH

THERE was once a very rich king named Midas. The columns of his palace were inlaid with gold, and his treasure room was filled with jewels, yet he was not satisfied. He longed for even greater wealth. He did not care for music or flowers, or indeed for anything else except his riches and his beautiful little daughter.

Midas wished to give his daughter, Marigold, the finest dresses ever made, the most beautiful beads and jeweled bands for her hair. This was one reason why he was glad to have gold and riches.

But Marigold loved to wear a short white frock, and to go barefoot over the grass with only a band of ribbon on her head. She liked to feel the cool wind blow through her curls; she loved roses and violets much better than jewels. Sometimes she begged King Midas to leave his treasure room, where he liked to sit, to walk in the woods with her.

"The birds are singing," she would say, "and the very first anemones are in bloom."

But Midas would pat her head and tell her to run out and play—just as all busy fathers have told their little girls ever since.

One day, as Midas sat counting his riches, a stranger walked into the room and touched him on the shoulder. Vines twined around the visitor's head, and a leopard skin hung from his shoulders.

"Who are you?" cried Midas in alarm, "and how did you pass the guards?"

"I am Bacchus, God of Wine and Gayety," said the stranger. "I have come to thank you. Not long ago you were kind to my old teacher, Silenus. The gods do not forget such things."

Then Midas remembered that one evening an aged man had stumbled into the palace. Midas had given him shelter and food and fresh clothing. In the morning the king had sent him on his way with a companion to guide him.

Midas rose to his feet—because even a royal mortal stands in the presence of the gods—and bowed low to Bacchus, inviting him to be seated. Bacchus looked at the chair inlaid with gold. He saw the table strewn with jewels and coins and glittering bowls. He shuddered and moved farther away from Midas.

"I cannot stay in this room," said Bacchus. "There is no sunshine here, nor any sound of the wind in the vine leaves."

Midas looked at the god in amazement.

"You talk like my daughter, Marigold," said he. "True, there is no sunshine here, but look! See the golden lights on these bowls, and the red glow on the jewels!"

"Have you seen the colors of grapes when the sun shines through them, purple and red and amber?" asked Bacchus.

"No," said Midas, "I like grapes only when they are brought to me on a golden platter. There is nothing in the world so lovely as gold. I wish everything I touch might be changed into that beautiful metal. Then I should be happy."

"You shall have your wish," said Bacchus, hurrying away out of the gloomy room to his vineyards on the sunny hills.

"I shall have my wish!" whispered Midas delightedly. "Can he really mean it?"

Just then the palace servants struck the big gong and called the king to dinner.

Midas locked the door of his treasury and walked toward the room where his dinner awaited him. He glanced down at the great key in his hand. It was gold! His sleeve, too, gleamed a dull yellow and felt stiff to his touch. His girdle was changed into the same metal. His sandals, everything he wore, was shining gold.

He touched a marble column as he passed, and it turned yellow. The curtains that he brushed in passing grew rigid and gleaming.

Marigold came dancing in from the woods, her hands full of white anemones. She sat down in her tall chair beside the king's.

"Why, Father," she said, "when did you buy that funny stiff robe? And your yellow sandals, where did you get them?"

Midas smiled delightedly as he sat down. "They are solid gold, my dear! The gods have given me the Golden Touch. You may have anything in the world that you wish."

"Look at your chair, Father!" cried Marigold.

"No doubt it also is gold," said Midas, smiling, and turning to look. "It seems more comfortable than ever. I shall have every chair in the palace made over."

He took his white napkin in his hand and shook it out. It was wonderful to see the golden color spread over the snowy linen, almost as if a yellow flame ran up the folds.

Smiling more than ever, he reached for his spoon. "We shall have all the golden dishes we like," he said.

Then he raised a spoonful of the savory soup to his mouth. He tasted it, and it was very good. But oh, horrible! When he tried to swallow it the taste vanished and there was nothing in his mouth but a hard lump. He choked and sputtered and coughed.

He looked at his plate in surprise.

Marigold put her arms around his neck and her cheek to his

"Can there be a stone in my soup?" he wondered. Midas tried another spoonful, but the same thing happened. He broke a piece of white bread, and it turned to gold as he raised it to his lips. He touched an apple and a pear. They became hard and glittering.

"Oh!" shouted the king, "I do not want my food to become gold. Everything else, O great god Bacchus, but not my food!"

Bacchus did not hear. He was far away in his vineyards listening to Pan's music. Marigold climbed down from her tall chair, and ran to the king.

"O dear Father," she said, "what has happened?"

She put her arms around his neck and her cheek to his. At the same moment her skin grew dark and yellow. The pink and white of her cheek vanished. Only her hair remained its own color, for her curls had always been like spun gold.

Midas put his hand on her to caress her, then drew away in terror. For his little daughter was now cold and hard, a golden statue.

"O Bacchus, O great Bacchus!" cried Midas, leaping to his feet, "take away this dreadful gift. My daughter has become a golden image. Everything I touch grows hard and cold. Give me back my little girl, or let me die!"

Bacchus heard at last, and came down from the hilltop and entered the palace.

"Well, Midas," he asked, "do you still care so much for gold?"

"No, no!" said the king. "Take away the Golden Touch and give me my Marigold."

Bacchus smiled wisely at the king.

"Perhaps now you will like the sunshine as much as gold," said the god, "and the glowing lights in grapes better than the glitter of stones. Perhaps now you will leave your treasure room sometimes and walk in the woods with Marigold."

"I will, I will!" promised Midas. "Only let her live again!"

"Then go to the river and wash," said Bacchus.

Midas ran as fast as he could out of the room and down the marble steps, which turned to gold as he passed. In the garden, the rose bushes that he brushed lost their green color and became tawny yellow. The gravel path changed, and the grass where he walked showed his footprints in yellow tracks.

Down the river bank Midas stumbled, and splashed into the water. His garments became soft and white. His girdle

and sandals were of leather once more. But the river sands where he washed became golden and remained so forever.

He ran back to the palace and took the golden figure of little Marigold in his arms. At first she felt hard and cold to his touch, but in a moment Marigold's arms moved, her color returned, and she grew soft and warm.

"O Father," she said, "I had a strange dream. I dreamed that I could not speak, or move, or—"

"Never mind, my sweetheart," said the king, "that is all over."

"And I dreamed that your robe was made of gold —"

"But see, it is soft white linen now," said Midas. "Let us eat."

The servants brought more hot food, and Midas and his daughter finished their dinner. Never had soup tasted so good to him, nor fruit so juicy. His napkin seemed more beautiful in its snowy whiteness than any golden fabric he had ever seen.

When they rose from the table, Marigold showed him the white anemones.

"There are whole banks of them in the woods," she said. "And when the sun shines on them, and the wind blows, they look just like little dancing nymphs with yellow hair and white tunics. Won't you come with me and see them?"

"Indeed, yes," said Midas.

He put his hand in Marigold's and walked with her to the woods. There he found more happiness than he had ever known in his treasure room, and learned to love the white buds of flowers more than the largest pearls in his treasure chest.

TRANSFORMATIONS

THE gods were very fond of transforming, or changing, the shape of things. They loved to come down to earth, disguised in different ways, and walk around and listen to everything that went on.

When a human being offended them, they changed him into something unpleasant. But often when the gods saw a man in danger, they helped him to escape by changing him into a tree or an animal. The punishments of the gods were severe. Sometimes, for even a little thing such as breaking the branches of a tree, they would imprison a mortal forever.

DRYOPE

Dryope was a beautiful Greek woman whom the gods punished harshly. One day Dryope and her sister went walking to gather flowers along the river. Dryope carried her baby boy in her arms, and beside them ran Iole, her sister, gathering myrtle and violets, never guessing what would happen before they returned.

147

Soon Dryope grew tired carrying her baby, and sat down to rest on a grassy bank beside the water. Near her a lovely lotus tree drooped its branches over the water, and the baby reached his hands toward the purple flowers.

Dryope picked some of the clusters and gave them to the baby, and Iole had just reached her hand to gather another cluster when they noticed purple drops falling from the broken stems.

Just then an aged wood-gatherer came by, and raising his hands in horror said that the nymph Lotis lived in this tree. They had broken the branches and now the nymph would die. Surely the gods would send a terrible punishment.

As he spoke, Dryope felt a strange stiffness come into her feet, and bark began to creep upwards over her body. Branches sprang from her two arms, and she could no longer fold them around the baby, who fell tumbling to the grass.

Iole clung to her sister as if she would hold back the brown bark that crept over her.

Soon a young lotus tree stood in Dryope's place. Only her face remained among the branches and looked sadly down on her baby and her sister.

She begged that Iole would bring the baby every day to play under the tree, and charged her especially to teach him never to break a branch or to pick a flower. As she spoke the leaves spread over her face, and Dryope was completely hidden by the tree.

To be shut up like this forever seems terrible, but no doubt Dryope soon began to feel like the nymphs who chose trees for their dwellings.

When the sun came up each morning and shone on her

Dryope picked some of the clusters and gave them to the baby

leaves, she must have felt a comforting warmth. In midsummer, she must have been glad when the rain came dropping on her boughs. And how happy and proud must Dryope have felt in blossom time, when every one of her boughs hung heavy with white and purple flowers!

Each day her little boy was carried to the river bank to talk with his mother in the lotus tree, and her branches would reach down and touch him with a caress.

When he was no longer a baby, her son still came to the tree. Even when he grew up, he sat in its shade to rest and to tell his mother about his happiness, his troubles, and his victories.

CLYTIE

Sometimes the gods changed people into other forms out of kindness. There was the water nymph Clytie who once saw Apollo as, with his sister Diana, he went hunting through the forest.

Apollo was the most beautiful of all the gods. Clytie had never seen anyone so splendid or so glorious. She loved him at once. But Apollo hurried by without even noticing her as she stood beside her little stream.

Clytie followed him, hoping that he would speak to her. But the hunting party soon reached the edge of the wood, and Apollo rose in a pale cloud, and disappeared toward the east.

The sky was gray, and there had been no sunshine all morning because Apollo, God of the Sun, hunting on earth, had not driven his chariot across the heavens.

Their yellow heads followed Apollo's chariot across the sky

Clytie watched the gray sky longingly. In a little while the mist began to scatter, and a pale yellow glow ran around the curving edges of the clouds. Then, with a burst of light, the chariot of the sun appeared, midway on its course.

"That is his chariot," said poor Clytie with a sigh, as she sat down on the ground to watch it.

All afternoon she watched it. Every day for nine days she sat in the same place, looking upward and longing for Apollo to come to earth that she might see his face.

She forgot to eat and grew thinner and thinner.

At last the gods grew sorry for her and changed her into a great golden sunflower. Her seeds spread over the earth and grew. Wherever the sun shown, they raised their yellow heads to its light and turned, now east, now west, forever following the course of Apollo's chariot as it passed across the sky.

NARCISSUS

Sometimes the gods made transformations just to amuse themselves—neither for punishment nor for the protection of mortals, but just for a little joke.

Narcissus was a youth who was so lovely that he was almost like a girl in his appearance. Like Clytie, he fell in love and pined without eating, day after day.

It was not a beautiful sea nymph whom Narcissus loved, nor a wood nymph, nor a mountain nymph, nor even a Greek maiden.

He fell in love with a face he saw in the water. He thought it was the face of a beautiful water sprite. He stayed at the

Echo answered Narcissus as he talked to the face in the water

bank, pleading with the lovely being, begging it to come out of the water and speak to him. Of course, it was only his own face that he saw reflected in the water, but Narcissus did not know it, because he had never seen his face in a mirror.

The nymph Echo loved Narcissus. She hid herself near him, and answered as he talked to the face in the water.

Echo would have told Narcissus he was in love with his own reflection, but she was being punished by Juno for talking too much. She could not speak unless someone else spoke first, and then only the same words she had heard.

When he said, "You are beautiful," Echo replied ever so softly, "You are beautiful," and poor Narcissus thought it was the water sprite who spoke. When he said, "I love you," the voice answered and, as he reached his arm into the water, instantly the face would vanish.

Then Narcissus thought the water nymph had fled from him. So he would call again and again, watching the water until it grew smooth and the face returned. All the time Echo would answer him in her sweet voice.

Narcissus stayed by the river, growing thinner and more unhappy. The gods came by in different forms and watched him. They listened to the strange conversation between Narcissus and Echo and thought it funny.

They laughed about it together when they gathered on Mount Olympus. Just as a bit of fun, when Narcissus grew so thin that he was ready to die, the gods changed him into a beautiful flower, which leaned forever over the river bank to look at its reflection in the water.

ERYSICHTHON AND THE OAK TREE

THERE was once a mortal named Erysichthon who would not believe all the stories of the gods' transformations. He went stamping through the woods, picking flowers and breaking trees. Just by good fortune he happened not to injure any tree that held a nymph or a dryad. But one day he went to chop wood in a sacred grove, and selected the biggest and most beautiful oak tree of all—the one around which the dryads and wood sprites loved best to play.

The grove belonged to the goddess Ceres, who made the grain and barley grow, and who watched over all the fruits and vegetables. Everyone was especially careful not to make Ceres angry for fear that she might spoil the harvest.

Erysichthon's companions would not touch the trees in Ceres's grove, because they were afraid. But Erysichthon boasted that it did not matter to him if Ceres herself were in a tree, he would cut whichever one he liked.

So he set his axe to the wood. The great oak trembled, and blood flowed from the wound he had made, but Erysichthon paid no attention and kept on chopping.

One of his friends seized Erysichthon's arm and begged

155

A friend seized Erysichthon's arm and begged **him** to stop

him to stop. But Erysichthon struck him with the axe and chopped harder than ever.

Then a clear sad voice spoke from among the branches. "I am a nymph," said the voice, "and beloved by Ceres. I have died by your hand, and I warn you that punishment will be sent you."

The others fled from the grove in terror, but Erysichthon swung his axe until the oak leaned over, creaking and groaning as great trees do when they are felled.

The tree, as it fell, crashed through the grove, and swept a dozen smaller trees to the earth. Erysichthon wiped his forehead and went home to dinner.

The wood nymphs had been watching from behind the trees. Now they went quickly to Ceres and told her what had happened. She was so angry that she called an oread from the mountain and sent her with a message to Famine, who lived far away on a wild crag.

Oreads were mountain nymphs who could travel from one mountain top to another by merely floating across. The oread told Famine what Erysichthon had done, and Famine flew swiftly downward to his house.

Erysichthon had eaten and thrown himself down to rest on his couch when Famine floated into the room unseen and hovered over his head. She folded her black cloak about him and breathed her poison into his veins. While he slept he dreamed of being hungry, and when he wakened shouted loudly for food.

Erysichthon's lovely daughter brought him bread and meat, but when he had eaten it he felt hungrier than ever. He called for more and still felt famished. His daughter brought plate after plate of hot food, wondering more and more at her father's strange appetite.

At last everything in the house was eaten; and still Erysichthon walked about looking for something more. He went into the garden and ate the vegetables from the ground and the fruit on the trees. He ate the buds of the flowers, and angrily bade his daughter hurry to the fisherman to get some fish, and to the shepherds to have them prepare a lamb. He could think of nothing but eating.

After a few days, Erysichthon had eaten all the food he owned, and spent all of his gold to buy more. He sold his beds and chairs and tables and his daughter's jewelry.

At last he sold his daughter herself to be a servant. When she heard what her father had done she went down to the sea and prayed to Neptune to protect her.

The god of the sea heard her prayer and came quickly to help her. His dolphin bore him over the waves with the speed of the wind, and he changed the daughter of Erysichthon into a young fisherman, so that neither her new master nor her father could find her.

Erysichthon at last died of hunger, and then Neptune changed his daughter back into her own form.

CIRCE AND ULYSSES

THERE was once a lovely enchantress named Circe. Her palace stood in a grove on a beautiful island. Here she lived alone and spent her time in studying magic. She learned all sorts of sorcery and tricks, and became so clever that she could turn men into whatever beasts she liked.

When strangers landed on her island, she changed them into lions and wolves and pigs. Her garden was full of enchanted animals that wandered back and forth, remembering that they were really men. They longed to speak, but could only grunt or growl. Her pigsties were crowded. But in all her palace there was no friend or servant, or any living person to keep her company.

One day a ship dropped anchor in the bay, and a band of sailors came wading ashore, looking for fresh water. Their leader was the great Ulysses. He was on his voyage home to Ithaca, in Greece, and had been through many dangers and hardships. His men were very hungry, and their clothes were ragged and travel-stained.

Ulysses climbed a hill so that he could look around him and decide if it would be safe for them to land at this island.

159

He saw no people and no houses of any sort, but only a thin
spiral of smoke rising from a distant grove. He hoped that this
was the fire of a friendly hearth. He went back to his men and
sent half of them, under a leader named Eurylochus, to ex-
plore the island. Ulysses and the rest of the crew stayed behind
to watch the boat.

Eurylochus led his men through the woods toward the
smoke, and at last they saw a beautiful palace, half hidden
by trees. The columns gleamed like white marble in the sun,
and a fountain sprayed into the air. The men were sure they
would be received with kindness in so fine a place.

But as they came still nearer they were terrified to see wild
animals roaming through the gardens. There were lions and
tigers and wolves walking sleepily back and forth among the
trees. Eurylochus and his comrades drew back and hid themselves where they could watch. They noticed that the animals
were drowsy and quiet. Soon the men gathered enough courage to move slowly toward the palace.

The beasts did not leap at them, or roar, but made low,
gentle sounds, and crowded around Eurylochus. They lay on
the ground at his feet and tried to lick his hands. He thought
he saw a pleading look in their eyes. Indeed, he had never before seen such eyes in any animals. They were like the eyes of
men in trouble.

He patted their heads and walked on toward the entrance
of the palace, where he heard music and the sound of singing.

He called out, to announce himself, and a lovely woman,
veiled in many garments, came floating toward him. Her thin
scarves fluttered in the soft wind, and her voice, as she invited
the strangers to enter, was low and sweet.

Eurylochus's comrades vanished and he saw only grunting pigs

They crowded into the palace, delighted at her welcome, but when Eurylochus looked into her eyes he saw they were small and cruel. He felt he would rather stay outside with the animals than follow her inside the huge door.

As the doors clanged together behind his comrades, the beasts in the garden uttered such mournful sounds that Eurylochus hid himself beside one of the windows. There he could see what happened in the palace and, perhaps, help his friends if they should, as he suspected, be in danger.

He saw them seated at a great banqueting table, with warm food and fruit before them, and all sorts of sweet things. While they ate, the air was filled with perfume and soft music. Eurylochus was very hungry himself, and the sight of the food almost made him wish that he had entered with his companions.

When the men had finished, they stretched themselves on the stone benches to rest, or sat sleepily in their chairs. Then their hostess took a little ivory wand in her hand and touched them very lightly, one by one. At once, long ears began to spring from their heads, and their bodies were covered with long hair. Hoofs took the place of their hands and feet, and they fell to the floor on all fours.

Before his eyes, Eurylochus's comrades vanished, and he saw only a dozen grunting pigs waddling around the banquet hall.

Then he knew that their lovely hostess was Circe, the enchantress. He understood now why the lions and tigers had looked at him so sadly, and had made such mournful sounds when the doors had closed behind his friends.

As he watched, he saw Circe lead her pigs out of the palace and shut them in a dirty sty. She threw them a bagful of acorns, and laughed at them, as they crowded to the fence, looking up at her pleadingly.

Eurylochus ran back to the ship and told the others what had happened. Ulysses at once started out to rescue his men, with his sword as his only weapon. As he hurried through the woods, the god Mercury appeared before him.

"However brave you may be," said the god, "your sword will not overcome the magic of Circe. But if you carry this sprig of green in your hand, it will keep you safe from her sorcery."

Mercury gave Ulysses a branch of a plant called moly, which grew only on Mount Olympus, and then he vanished. Carefully holding the green sprig, Ulysses entered the palace garden. The beasts crowded close around him and followed him to the door.

Circe herself came to meet him, much pleased to have another victim as handsome and strong as Ulysses.

She seated him at the banquet table, and smiled as she watched him eat, thinking what a fine large boar he would make. But when she touched him with her wand, the power of the little plant turned her magic aside.

Ulysses did not fall to the floor, nor waddle away, grunting. Instead he drew his sword and rushed at her, commanding her to release his friends.

Circe was so frightened that she knelt before him and begged him to spare her. She promised to free all her prisoners, even the lions and wolves in the garden. She agreed to help Ulysses on his journey, and to provide food and water for him to carry away in his ship.

She ran to the pigsties and, as she touched each one of the boars, it changed again into its own form.

The beasts in the garden became men, and spoke to each other once more in words instead of growls. All they wanted was to return to their own homes, their families and friends, and they began at once to make plans for their journey.

Circe kept her promise and helped Ulysses on his voyage. She provided him with much good food and drink, and warned him of dangers that he might meet on the sea.

When she saw that the clothes of Ulysses and his friends were travel-stained and worn, she gave them beautiful robes from her own chests. Circe made a new sail for their boat, and was kept so busy that for the time being she forgot to think of her evil magic arts.

At last everything was ready for Ulysses's departure. The ship, with its white sail, lay floating near the shore. The men put on their fresh robes. Then they carried on board jugs of water and wine, sacks of meal, smoked meat, and all the other things they might need on the voyage.

The men seized the oars in their hands. The sail filled with wind, and with Circe's help, Ulysses sped away from the island toward Ithaca, his home.

NAUSICAA AND ULYSSES

ONCE there was a princess who lived by the sea. Her father was King Alcinoüs, who ruled the country of the Phaeacians, a land dear to the gods, peopled by noble men and lovely women.

The Phaeacians were wonderful seamen who knew the unmarked paths of the sea as a shepherd knows the tracks upon his mountain. They knew the ways of the winds and tides, and in all the world there were no sailors so brave and wise, or any ships so strong, as those of the Phaeacians.

Nausicaa, the princess, loved to look out over the water and watch her father's ships as they flew, full-sailed, toward foreign lands, or skimmed homeward like white-winged gulls.

One day there came a dreadful storm which swept the coast of the Phaeacian land. Great crested waves came rolling in. The wind blew so fiercely that not even the gulls could fly against it, but rested on the water and rode up and down with the waves.

Far out on the sea, strong ships fought the storm and hurried toward their harbors. But there was one craft without sail, and without oars or rudder, that the waves tossed here

Ino, as a gull, flew to the raft with a veil for Ulysses

and there at will. It was the raft of the hero Ulysses. Weary and tempest-tossed, he clung to the wet, creaking logs and prayed to the gods for help. The waves washed over him and pounded against his body. His arms were aching with weariness.

Neptune, God of the Sea, did not heed Ulysses's prayer for he was angry with the hero. But Ino, a sea nymph, felt pity for Ulysses and, taking the form of a gull, she flew to the raft and spoke thus:

"Unhappy man, Neptune is full of wrath, and the storm may destroy your raft. Then you will drown, for no mortal can swim against this sea. But here is a veil that I shall give you. Wind it about your breast and you cannot perish. When you reach the shore, unwind it and throw it into the sea, and it will come back to me."

She gave him the veil, and with a flash of white wings dived into the sea and the waves swept over her.

Then, just as she had warned him, the raft was broken and the logs were washed apart. Ulysses was cast into the sea, but because of the magic veil, he breasted the waves safely. For two nights and two days he rode the angry waters.

On the morning of the third day, the wind fell and the sun rose and Ulysses beheld the welcome sight of land. But when he drew nearer, he heard the crashing of waves on rocks, and knew that he could not reach shore. Swimming a little distance, he at last saw the mouth of a river, and prayed to the river god.

"Hear me, O River," he cried, "I flee from the anger of Neptune. Pity me and help me in my need."

As he swam toward the river, he felt the water become

smoother and warmer. There were no rocks here to make his landing dangerous. So at last Ulysses came to shore.

He loosed the scarf which the sea nymph had given him and tossed it back into the ocean, so that it might return to its owner. Then, bruised and weary, he crawled up into a clump of low bushes that grew near the mouth of the river, made himself a bed of leaves, and lay down and slept.

It happened that it was in the land of the Phaeacians that Ulysses lay down to rest. Minerva, who watches over heroes, went to the palace of King Alcinoüs and, passing unseen through all the doors, came to the chamber of Nausicaa, the king's daughter.

Minerva stood beside the sleeping princess, and in a dream bade her go with her maidens down to the river's mouth and wash her garments and the linen of the household.

When Nausicaa awakened, she sought her father as he was departing for the council of the Phaeacians. She asked him for the wagon and the mules in order to go to the river and wash the garments and linen of the household.

Her father called the servants, and they made ready the wagon and harnessed the mules. Her maidens brought the soiled garments and loaded them into the cart.

Then Nausicaa's mother put in a basket of food and an urn of the sweet juice of grapes, also a jar of olive oil so that they might rub themselves after they had bathed.

Nausicaa mounted to her seat and drove the mules. Her maidens followed, singing, until they came to where the fresh water of the river emptied into the sea.

They untied the bundles of clothing, dipped them in the river, and rubbed them on the smooth stones. They rinsed them and spread them on the grass to dry. All this time, at a little distance, the hero Ulysses lay sleeping, hidden by the bushes.

When Nausicaa and her maidens had finished their tasks and bathed, they put on fresh linen and ate the meal that Queen Arete had prepared. Then they played ball, leaping and laughing and calling to each other until at last, in a particularly joyful moment, they shrieked so loudly that Ulysses awakened. He sat up, smiling to feel the warm sunshine, and very thankful for being safe on land.

He saw the girls playing by the river and the white clothing drying on the grass. He longed for just one length of linen to cover himself, so that he might go near them and ask them on what shore he had been shipwrecked and where to find help. But the garments were so far away that he could not reach them without leaving the bushes. He broke some large branches and, holding them in front of him, walked toward the girls. They saw him coming and, screaming louder than ever, ran away as fast as they could.

Only Nausicaa did not run away from him. She knew in a moment that here was someone who had been shipwrecked and needed help; so she stood waiting for Ulysses to speak.

She was so beautiful that Ulysses thought she might be a goddess, perhaps Diana herself. He told her that she was lovely as a blossom, and like a palm tree that he had once seen at Delos, so straight and slender, yet swaying with the wind. He asked her the name of the country, and told her that he had been shipwrecked.

Nausicaa knew that Ulysses must be a great hero, for his bearing and his speech were like those of a king. She answered in the words of a princess, and promising him help, called her maidens back from the meadow.

She gave Ulysses a garment of her brother's so that he might clothe himself, and her maidens brought him the jar of olive oil. Ulysses went along the river bank a little distance, bathed, and rubbed the oil on his swollen shoulders and his bruised hands. He put on the fresh garment and returned to where Nausicaa stood with her maidens. Then they gave him meat and cakes and sweet wine.

As he ate, they gathered the dry clothes and folded them and put them into the mule cart. Nausicaa mounted to her seat and bade Ulysses follow.

Ulysses lingered in the grove of Minerva and came

"But when you come near the city," she said, "wait in the grove of Minerva outside the walls, and do not come into the city until I have reached my father's home. Then enter and ask the way to the palace of the king. When you have found it, pass quickly through the court and the chambers to where my mother sits at her weaving. My father will be there also, but pass by his seat and kneel before my mother and ask her aid. If you do this you will be helped by my people, and find welcome and a way of returning to your own land."

Ulysses remembered these commands. He lingered in the grove of Minerva and came at last, in the evening, to the palace of King Alcinoüs.

at last, in the evening, to the palace of King Alcinoüs

Never had Ulysses seen such splendor, even in his own dear land of Ithaca. The doors were of gold, and the fluted columns of silver. There was a garden near the door with everbearing trees of olives and figs and apples. There were grapes—purple, red, and green. And in this garden, when apples or figs or olives were picked, fresh fruit immediately grew upon the branches of the trees; so that there was no fruitless winter in the land of the Phaeacians.

Ulysses entered the noble doors and came to the chamber where Queen Arete sat. He knelt before her and clasped her knees. He begged that she would have pity and help him on his way. When he had finished, he sat down in the lowliest seat among the ashes by the hearth and bowed his head.

The king took him by the hand and raised him from where he sat, and led him to a seat of honor. The housekeeper brought bread and wine and sweetmeats and set them before Ulysses.

Now, as he ate, Queen Arete looked closely at him. She noticed well his kindly manner and his noble form, and she saw also that he wore a garment of her own weaving and her own sewing.

She wondered greatly at this, and spoke to Ulysses, saying, "Who are you? Did you not tell me that you came across the sea? And if you came that way, who gave you the robe you are wearing?"

Then Ulysses told the queen all that had happened, how Nausicaa had helped him and given him the garment, and had told him to follow her to the palace.

Arete and Alcinoüs were not displeased, but welcomed the stranger with honor. They prepared a banquet and invited the councilors and nobles of the land, and there were games and songs and tests of strength.

Then Alcinoüs bade his people fit out a large, strong ship, and man it with fifty-two noble youths.

Ulysses departed from the land of the Phaeacians carrying many gifts, and boarded the ship that Alcinoüs had loaned him. The sailors pushed off with their oars, and the sails filled with wind. As long as the boat could be seen the Princess Nausicaa waved to him and wished him a safe voyage and a happy return to his home.

Ulysses was weary with his long wanderings. He saw that the Phaeacian seamen were skilled and needed no help, so he stretched himself upon the deck and slept.

When the ship drew near the shores of Ithaca, the kindly sailors did not wake him, but lifted him gently and waded ashore with him and laid him, still sleeping, on the sand. Beside him they put the gifts of King Alcinoüs and Queen Arete, jewels and golden dishes from the king, and fine, beautifully dyed cloth that Nausicaa and the queen had woven and colored with their own hands.

Then they departed and turned their ship and sailed homeward, leaving Ulysses asleep on the shore, safe in his own land.

POMONA AND VERTUMNUS

POMONA was a nymph who took care of the fruit-bearing trees of the orchards. While her sisters watched over the trees of the forests, Pomona worked among her apple trees, her pear trees, and her vines. She pruned and tended them from dawn until dark. She led little streams to water their roots, and cut off the long useless shoots.

She trained the grape vines to climb on the trunks of elm trees, so that they spread among the branches until the elms looked as though they were full of blue and amber grapes.

Many lovers came wooing Pomona—the fauns and satyrs, who were part man, part goat, and even the god Pan. His legs were like a goat's, but he played such music on his pipes that the nymphs would have no one else to play for their dancing.

Pomona would not think of romance or of wedding anyone. She cared only for her garden and her fruit trees. She gave her suitors gifts of fruit and sent them all away.

The country people around her, who had gardens of their own, were a great trouble to Pomona. They tried to steal her fruit, and cut shoots from her trees to graft on their

174

Pomona offered her largest, reddest apples to the old woman

own. So she built a high wall around her garden and allowed
no suitors or idle country folk to enter through the little gate.
After the wall was built her lovers grew discouraged, except
one who loved her more than the others did.

His name was Vertumnus, and he was the God of the
Changing Seasons. He possessed the power of taking any form
he wished. Sometimes he pretended to be a reaper, and came
to Pomona's gate with a basket of corn to sell. At other times
he would carry a pruning hook, and offer to climb the highest
trees and to trim the branches that Pomona could not reach.
On other days he dressed like a fisherman, and brought her
little spotted trout from the streams. In these ways he was
allowed to come in through the gate and visit Pomona each
day, until he grew to love her more than ever.

Once he came as an aged woman, who wore a dark cloak
and asked permission to enter the garden and see the fruit.
Pomona smiled, and swung the gate wide open. She led the
old woman to a grassy bank, and helped her to seat herself
beneath a tree. She gathered her largest and reddest apples
and offered them to her visitor.

"Do you tend this garden all alone?" asked the woman.
When Pomona said that she did, the old woman cried, "What!
have you not chosen a suitor? Do you mean to live alone like
this forever?"

Pomona smiled and said that she cared more for her
garden than for any youth, and that she liked to live alone.
Then the aged stranger pointed to an elm tree on which Pomona had trained her grapes.

"If yonder vine were not twined around the elm," she
said, "it would lie on the ground. The sun could never reach

the grapes to ripen them and make them grow. You are like the vine, and I will tell you of someone who is like the elm."

The old woman then began to praise Vertumnus.

"No one is stronger, or kinder, or more beautiful than he, and like yourself, he delights in gardening."

She talked so long of this suitor that at last Pomona became interested and almost wished to see him.

Then the old woman craftily began to tell Pomona the story of Anaxarete: how that noble lady scorned her lovers and would marry no one, until at last, in despair, the most ardent of them, named Iphis, killed himself for love of her, and Anaxarete was turned to stone as a punishment for her hardness.

Then, with a laugh, the old woman added, "Beware lest your own coldness bring you a like fate!"

As she spoke her dark cloak fell from her, her wrinkles vanished, her bent shoulders straightened, and Vertumnus himself stood before Pomona.

When he spoke, it was in a voice very different from that of the old woman. Pomona thought it more beautiful than any voice she had ever heard.

As she led him around the garden, Pomona said, "You are indeed like the elm tree, and I would rather be like the vine than like the noble lady Anaxarete."

NIOBE

THERE was once a queen named Niobe. She was rich and very proud of her beautiful kingdom and her many possessions, but especially of her seven sons and seven daughters.

Niobe clothed them in linen of purple and scarlet. Her handmaidens embroidered their robes with rich patterns. They wore jewels and ornaments of gold. When the seven princes and their sisters went walking together, they looked like a moving garden of bright poppies.

One day the people of Thebes held a festival in honor of the goddess Latona, who was the mother of Diana and Apollo. The women and children put on their best robes and wore wreaths of laurel on their heads. They carried offerings of flowers and fragrant oils to the altar in Latona's temple.

Niobe, riding through Thebes in her chariot, watched them on their way to the festival. Usually, as Niobe's chariot passed, the people threw flowers before her and bowed low in honor of their queen. But today they bowed less deeply and hurried on to the temple, carrying their flowers to the goddess.

Niobe drove to the temple and watched them enter.

Niobe, in her chariot, watched them on their way to the festival

"What folly is this?" she asked. "Why should Latona be honored with worship and none be paid to me?"

"This is the day of Latona's festival," they answered. "We pay homage to her, for she is the mother of Apollo, God of the Sun, and of Diana, who guides the moon."

When Niobe heard this, she compared her own fourteen children with Latona's two. Like all mothers, she thought her children more beautiful and wiser and more glorious than any other children. She drew herself up with pride and anger and spoke to her people.

"I, your queen," she said, "have fourteen children, seven sons and seven daughters. Were I to lose some of my children, I should still be richer than Latona, who has only two. Put off the laurel from your brows—have done with this worship!"

When Niobe spoke no one dared disobey. They put down their burdens of flowers and their gifts. They took off their wreaths of laurel and, leaving Latona's temple strewn with unplaced offerings, they returned to their homes.

Niobe drove proudly away to her palace, not knowing that Latona herself had been present, invisible in the temple. She had come to attend the festival, and was now filled with a great anger against Niobe for interrupting the worshipers.

She returned to the Cynthian mountain top where she dwelt. There she sought her children, Diana and Apollo, and told them to punish Niobe for what she had done. Apollo and Diana took their sharpest arrows and went to a hill overlooking the city of Thebes.

On a wide plain outside the city Niobe's seven sons were engaged in different sports. Ismenos, the eldest, was driving his chariot. An arrow struck him as he guided his foaming steeds, and dropping the reins he fell lifeless.

One brother now fled, urging his horses to greater speed, but an arrow overtook him as he rode. Another ran to his aid, and fell. Two brothers were wrestling, and one arrow pierced them both.

One of the younger boys sat watching his elder brothers from a little distance. He was astonished at their fall, and

Diana's arrow flew through the air. One after

thought this was some strange new game. But another arrow sped from Apollo's bow, and he fell backward and lay lifeless like the others.

Only one was left, Ilioneus. He prayed to the gods to save him. Apollo would have spared Ilioneus but the arrow had already left the string, and it was too late.

Then Niobe, sitting in her palace, heard sounds of wailing and mourning. Her attendants came to tell her what had happened. She rushed to the plain with her daughters and found the bodies of her seven sons stretched where they had fallen.

Although she could not see Diana and Apollo, she guessed that this terrible punishment had come from the gods. But her spirit was still proud. She gathered her seven daughters close to her and, raising her eyes to heaven, cried out:

another, Niobe's lovely daughters dropped beside her

"Cruel Latona! Satisfy your rage with my suffering. Yet, great as is my loss, I am still richer than you, my conqueror."

Again they heard the sound of a bow, and Diana's arrow flew through the air. And now, one after another, Niobe's lovely daughters dropped beside her until only the youngest was left.

Niobe was proud no longer. She fell on her knees, and with one arm around the little princess, stretched the other toward the hill from which the arrows had come.

"Spare me this last and youngest child," she cried. But the arrow had left Diana's bow, and in a moment the youngest princess lay beside the others. Niobe never left the plain, but bowed her head and wept day after day until at last the gods pitied her grief and changed her into a rock. But still she wept, and ever afterward a tiny stream trickled from the stone, the sign of her never-ending sorrow.

ENDYMION

ONCE there were two shepherds who watched their flocks on Mount Latmos. One was a mortal, young and beautiful, who tended his sheep on the grassy slopes beside sparkling streams, and sang as he kept his lambs from straying into the forest. The other was Pan, God of Forests, Pastures, Flocks, and Shepherds. He pastured his flock deep in the woods in a secret glade.

Sometimes Endymion, the mortal shepherd, was lonely, and the days seemed long to him. Then he found comfort in his thoughts. They came trooping to bear him company, gay and beautiful and sad—thoughts that danced and floated like nymphs, and some, like a child singing, so beautiful that they brought tears to his eyes.

Endymion gathered all these thoughts and wove them into poems and songs. They kept him company on Mount Latmos. They were like a band of friends and he was no longer lonely.

Sometimes at night when Diana passed over Mount Latmos in a glory of light, she would hear the faint sound of piping and think, "That is Pan, in the forest, playing on his pipes."

Then again Diana would hear a clear, high song, and would wonder; for though Pan could make sweet music on his pipes, his voice was deep and rough.

For many nights Diana delighted in these songs without beholding the singer. At last she saw Endymion sitting beside a stream with his flock near by. The silver rays of her moonlight shone over him and sparkled on the water at his feet.

Then a strange thing happened to Diana; for the first time she knew the beginning of love. Instead of journeying on through the heavens toward the ocean, she paused above Mount Latmos.

Half the night she stayed to watch Endymion and to hear him sing. The beauty of the sky and the silver light around him filled Endymion with such happiness that he sang as he never had done before.

And Diana, whose heart had never before turned toward god or mortal, felt a longing to be with Endymion and a tenderness for him, a wish to bring him happiness and to save him from pain and sorrow forever.

In the last part of the night Endymion slept, and Diana moved on across the sky to brighten the dark waters of the sea. At dawn she drew the purple cloud curtains over the moon, and hurried back to earth, to climb the dewy slopes of Latmos. Again she listened to Endymion, and called her nymphs to hear him and to tend his flocks.

Sometimes through the day Endymion wondered that his sheep stayed so near him and fed so peacefully without

Diana watched him and thought how short a while he would be young

straying. He did not know that unseen nymphs kept watch over the flock so that he might be free to sing, nor did he see Diana herself at his side. He only felt a strange and pleasing comfort, and a happiness so great that it seemed as though his heart would break.

Diana watched him as he sang, and thought how short a while Endymion would be beautiful and young and full of songs. She thought of all the sad things that had happened to other mortals and that would also come to Endymion—pain and old age and death.

So she rose and left him and went to Olympus and sought Jupiter, her father, as he sat on his throne in the assembly room of the gods.

She told her father about the young shepherd, and begged him to give eternal youth to Endymion. But Jupiter reminded her that no mortal may have eternal youth except by falling into an everlasting sleep.

Then Diana's heart was troubled, for she knew that if Endymion slept forever, they could not roam the hills, and hunt and laugh and play together. But putting aside all thoughts of self, she asked for Endymion the gift of youth and eternal sleep, and Jupiter granted her wish.

Diana returned to Mount Latmos and, bending over Endymion, she wove around him the spell of slumber.

His sheep heard the soft echo of Pan's piping far off in the glade and strayed nearer and nearer to the forest. They heard no call from their shepherd, who lay asleep. So they disappeared unhindered into the woods and joined the flocks of Pan.

As he slept, Endymion dreamed that he roamed through

the gardens of the gods, or that he walked in the cool dim groves of the ocean over paths of white shells and coral. He saw small sea nymphs peep from behind purple sea anemones. He found the palaces of the sea nymphs and sat with them at their banquets. All these things Endymion dreamed, as he lay sleeping, free from the pain and sorrow of mortals and forever young and beautiful.

PYGMALION AND GALATEA

PYGMALION was a sculptor who could think of nothing but his chisels and the marble and ivory with which he loved to work. Beautiful Greek girls came walking by his window, and peeped in at the door to watch him, but he never raised his head or paid the least attention to them.

One day Pygmalion chose the largest, most perfect piece of ivory in the kingdom. When the laborers had brought it to his home, he took his keenest tools and began to carve the ivory with delicate care.

"There is no maiden living," said Pygmalion, "so beautiful as this statue that I shall make."

For weeks he worked, stopping only to eat, and at night to throw himself on the floor beside the statue to rest.

Day by day the figure grew more lovely. At last it seemed so perfect that nothing could be done to make it more wonderful. Still Pygmalion worked, smoothing and carving the ivory until it was indeed more beautiful than any Greek maiden in the land.

When the statue was finished, Pygmalion clothed it in soft garments and hung jewels around the ivory neck. He spent all his time admiring and adoring the figure he had made. He named it "Galatea," which means "Sleeping Love."

Just at this time there was in Pygmalion's city a festival in honor of Venus, the Goddess of Beauty and of Love. Pygmalion went to her temple. He offered gifts at her altar, and prayed that she would give him for his bride a living maiden exactly like his beautiful ivory statue.

Venus had been standing unseen beside her altar. When she heard Pygmalion's prayer, she left her temple and went to the sculptor's home to see the figure of which he was so fond.

The goddess was delighted with the loveliness of Pygmalion's statue. She thought it looked much like herself. This pleased her so that she touched the cold ivory and brought it to life.

She laid her fingers on the waving hair and it became soft and lustrous. The cheeks grew pink, the eyes blue, and the lips like coral.

When Pygmalion returned and entered his home, the statue no longer stood in its usual corner. Instead, a beautiful maiden with golden hair, and skin like ivory flushed with the color of sunrise walked toward him.

Pygmalion watched in amazement. When he saw that his statue lived and moved, he threw himself on the floor and clasped her feet. They were warm and rosy.

Galatea looked down at him, smiling and touching his hair with her slender fingers.

Pygmalion did not forget to offer thanks to the goddess. He built an altar to Venus of ivory and gold and carved it with all kinds of blossoms and birds.

Pygmalion named the finished statue Galatea, or Sleeping Love

Every day as long as Pygmalion and Galatea lived, they offered gifts at the altar, and Venus in return blessed them with happiness and love.

PRINTED IN U.S.A.